To Carol,
Hope you enjoy
memories. L
Carole,

REMNANTS OF A YOUTH CLUB

REMNANTS OF
A YOUTH CLUB

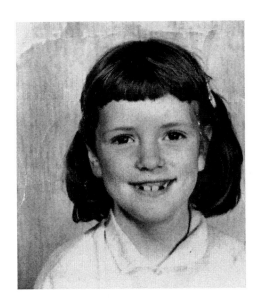

A story of lasting friendship
By

Alice Cachjeka

CREMER PRESS

First Published in Great Britain in 2005 by
Carole Hawke, Christine Thornton,
Jean White and Kath Coady under the joint pseudonym
of Alice Cachjeka.

ISBN 1 898722 54 4

Printed and bound in Great Britain by
Cremer Press, **Edmund Mercer**,
45 Harrison Street, Blackburn. Lancs. BB2 2JE.

ACKNOWLEDGEMENTS

Firstly we each wish to acknowledge our dear friend Margaret, who gave us the inspiration to put pen to paper.

To her husband Colin, we offer a most sincere thank you for allowing us to share tender moments.

We give deep thanks to Margaret's mother, Mrs. Hand, for without you, 'your daughters' would not have had a story to tell.

*A **'big'** thank you is due to our husbands and families, for their support throughout our grief. It was your encouragement that gave us the heart to tell our story.*

Grateful appreciation must go to Hayhurst Camera Shop, Nelson for their help with photographic work.

Thanks also go to our editor, Madeleine Fish. What would we have done without you?

Chapter One

'Oh the grand old Duke of York,
he had ten thousand men,
he marched them up to the top of the hill,
and he marched them down again'.

Picture the scene - twenty or so four-year old soldiers marching and saluting to their teacher, Mrs. Peel, while she bashed away at the keys of the old piano, with arms outstretched over her protruding belly, concealing her own future little soldier, for her baby was expected to enter the world within the next few weeks.

Mrs. Peel, her large bulge covered over with a loose, faded-blue, paisley smock, fascinated this little army. She was not the prettiest lady in the school, for her plainness made her appear much older than her actual years. Still, her small charges loved this warm, gentle-mannered woman. They felt a sense of untroubled security in this baby class, unaware of what fate held in store for them as they progressed into the juniors.

The year was 1956, the place dowdy St. Mary Magdalene's Infant School. It was dowdy on account of the greyish dense smoke that puffed its way from the train engines, which ran at regular intervals both day and night alongside the building, parallel with Haslam Street.

The visible vapour, which spiralled from the chimneys belonging to the rows of terraced properties, served to further drape the school and streets in gloom. These dwellings were the backdrop of the area. The smog which clung to the stone and mortar became a biochemical hazard, as it created a risk to the families who were housed there, and to the occupants of the school yard who played there.

Tiny metal-framed window-panes, cracked and peeling, cried out in desperate need of paint. They were mean windows, for even in high season, daylight was kept to a minimum. One third of the glass was frosted as if each had something to hide. The sun's rays were defeated in entering most of the classrooms, further emphasising the dismal atmosphere, which dwelt within.

Laughter exploded, the marching lost its rhythm, as one little female soldier was totally unaware that the gathered skirt of her red gingham frock was tucked inside her knickers. This is the first memory for Christine Mary and Carole Anne of their friend Margaret.

St. Mary Magdalene's was a regimented Roman Catholic institution, so badly in need of repair, and a rather poor excuse posing as a school serving the community. It was run by disciplinarian rules, and teachers who indoctrinated religion into young minds. This authoritarian attitude left its mark on the lives of many of the children who attended this school. Although this behaviour was deplored by many parents, it was also accepted by most as the 'norm' in the 1950's.

St. Mary Magdalene's pupils came from a variety of social backgrounds, but chiefly from the lower classes. However there were one or two families held in high regard by the clergy, because of their generous contributions to the church funds. This caused a certain amount of animosity and tarnished envy, owing to Margaret and her friend Geraldine Holsworth, both being cordially invited to have tea with the Bishop of Salford on a number of occasions.

One of the few good memories of this early period was going to sleep after dinner. The infants were put down to rest every afternoon on regulation fold down canvas beds, with grey prickly army blankets. This was especially beneficial to Christine Mary, who was only three-years old, having had to come to school a year early because of her older sister Carole Anne, (both names with an e) who had cried profusely when they were separated. From their first day at school they were known as the Trickett sisters. Crying a lot stemmed from total disharmony within the Trickett household.

Christine Mary was born on a bleak December morning in 1952, providing Carole Anne with an unexpected birthday present, as Mrs. Audrey Trickett's labour pains came earlier than expected. The swirling winds outside caused bitter cold draughts in the front bedroom of the council house, the birthing place for her child. Frosty patterns had already formed on the window-panes upstairs, creating a picturesque, but freezing winter scene, as icicles dangled from the jamb stones.

Wanting to welcome her child into a warm inviting room, Audrey pleaded with her father-in-law to carry some of the hot coals up from the fire in the black-leaded range that heated the living-room, which was aglow with a mixture of cinders and charred wood.

When he refused her this request, Audrey herself bravely strove to take the shovel from the coal-hole and collect some of the burning cinders. With clenched white knuckles she held onto the handrail, struggling upstairs in the throes of her excruciating labour pains. Somehow she carefully transported the burning cinders up the wooden stairs, trying to blank out what was happening to her, as she laid the hot coals into the grate of the small, black iron fireplace in the front bedroom.

Even informing the midwife was too much trouble for Granddad Trickett; his beverage at the local pub came first, rather than greeting his grandchild.

Carole Anne watched from her cot as Audrey struggled to fetch her baby into the world.

The snow lay like a thick carpet on the ground, making it difficult for travellers. Philip Trickett was due to arrive home in time for Christmas; he was already a day late owing to the atrocious weather. He was in the army and stationed down South. Christine Mary was not due to be born until *after* Christmas, but she was not giving her father time to get home on leave to witness her birth. She was coming early and waiting for no one. Christine Mary was born healthy and rosy, but weighing a mere four and a half pounds. Both mother and baby were admitted to the Isolation Ward at Bank Hall Maternity Hospital.

Sadly the consequence of this meant that poor Carole Anne was separated from her mother, as she was passed over to the care of the local orphanage to spend her Christmas with strangers. This had a profound affect on Carole Anne, for from then on, she needed to be around her family members in order to feel secure.

Life in post-war Lancashire was still difficult and challenging for most families, and the Trickett family was no exception. Audrey's father-in-law had suddenly departed from this life just six weeks after Christine Mary's birth. Philip was now at home, having been discharged from the army, and Audrey had since given birth to two sons, Stephen and Stuart. Life was as perplexing as ever with four children all under four years of age.

Although ration books had been discontinued, commodities remained in short supply. Housewives constantly juggled with finances in order to make ends meet. Supermarkets as we know them today, were then a thing for the future in the United Kingdom, with America being at the forefront of this conception. The grocer monopolised the market, by allowing families to have their goods now and settle up later, but with a large hidden interest, by means of charging extortionate prices. The bill was expected to be paid at the end of the week, when pay-day came around, hence, the saying *'put it on the slate'*. That was of course if the public house had not got the money first, as the male of the house was usually the sole financial provider.

The diet was basic to say the least; if you were lucky enough to have a good meal on Sunday, then you were guaranteed a hearty meal on Monday. This was known as bubble and squeak, and consisted of potatoes and cabbage, which tasted even better the second time around, having been fried in dripping.

In many households broth was cooked on Tuesday, then re-heated two or three times leading up to Friday, which in Catholic homes was a fasting day. This meant that no meat could be eaten, and fish was the alternative meal for those who could afford it. The workers in the household had fish, the rest of the family had chips and mushy peas, mopped up with a slice of bread.

Some provisions were quite rare indeed, one of these being instant coffee, which today we all take for granted. It was introduced in single-cup sachets. Was this perhaps a trial run, and the way of things to come? Up until this time coffee had been supplied in liquid form, and resembled dark thick treacle. Within two or three years it had appeared on the shelves of the shops in glass jars, and looked like gravy browning.

Gladys, a neighbour of Mrs. Trickett's, was once offered a cup of gravy in mistake for coffee, during one of the many times they spent together camping in their houses, gossiping and attempting to put the world to rights. Gladys, a mother of four children, was the agony aunt to all her neighbours, and never missed the opportunity of repeating someone else's misfortune. She was a somewhat comical individual, who possessed a voice, which was loud and throaty. She'd launch her words through toothless gums, to reveal a slight hint of a stammer. Being tall and slender should have given her grace; however for a woman only in her mid-forties, the wrinkled skin hung from her limbs like that of a wasted seventy-year old. Her hair was a mixture of dark strands and a generous amount of grey, with the overall colour appearing as slate. Once a week it was smoothed into place with a semi-permanent finger wave, held in place with a metal grip.

Weekdays, indoors or outdoors, Gladys could often be seen wearing a woven, woolly plaid headscarf, folded into a triangle, and tied in a double knot underneath her chin. Her attire usually consisted of a well-worn skirt and jumper, with its sleeves too baggy to be left loose, and so rolled several times, until the layers met up with her jagged elbows. As Gladys tasted her coffee she coughed and spluttered nearly choking, as this was a rare occasion when she was wearing her teeth.

At the same time she cursed, "Eh bloody hell Audrey, what the hell is this stuff you've given me? Are you trying to bloody poison me or what?"

This was to become a source of laughter for many years to come.

One winter Gladys invested in a pair of suede fur-lined, long boots. Even if the weather was clement she wore them. The carpet square was brushed, the linoleum long-mopped and disinfected, whilst Gladys still wore her winter boots. Later, sitting in a squat position, palms outstretched over glowing cinders, and a woodbine cigarette gripped in the corner of her pale thin lips, staring absent-mindedly at the black-leaded fire range, the boots would still be on her feet. Only when they became unrecognisable, through so much collected grease and grime, did Gladys finally give up her beloved boots. One can only imagine the amount of feudal animosity in the Trickett household, brought about by Gladys's precious footwear.

Audrey was wrapped in a blanket of green envy. It was smothering her. If only *she* could have been the proud owner of such footwear, and languished in such fashionable items, but for her times were harsh, and money was always short. These resentful jealous feelings, that Audrey could no longer control, blew up like an erupting volcano. Words of hurt and anger blasted at Philip and whichever one of the children was in her way.

Gladys's spouse Samuel, or Sammy as he was nicknamed, was of total contrast to his wife. Having served his time with the British Army, his frame had developed the muscles of an athlete. His face was tanned and leathery, with a cultured moustache lining his upper lip. He wore his black hair greased and sleeked from front to back, being proud to resemble the film idol Clarke Gable. A huge photograph of Sammy wearing his khaki uniform hung in a dark wood frame from the picture rail in the living-room - lest anyone forget!

These characters were the backbone of Stoops Estate, and although often embattled with one another, they were ever ready to embrace each other in times of need.

Stoops Estate was sprawled in avenues to the South-West perimeter of Burnley. These new houses had stretched themselves away from the poorer homes of St. Mary Magdalene's parish, yet came within the parish's remit. Not many families in this area were Roman Catholic, so Hargher Clough School served the majority of children.

Most tenants were exceedingly proud of their humble council houses; paths were swept, steps donkey-stoned and gardens lovingly nurtured. Beyond the gardens there lay some exceptional countryside. Two hills belonging to the Pennine Chain commanded the boundaries, as if fortresses in battle, protecting their armies. They stood opposing each other, like male and female, hot and cold.

Hambledon Hill was North facing, with its rugged, dark heathery colours. Gullies and crevices were dug deep from centuries of wind and rain, and the lack of penetration from the sun. The odd bleak farm nestled within its slopes looked uninviting to town folk.

Pendle Hill faced South, and was warming to the eye of the beholder. It stood splendid and mystical, surrounded by folklore and inspired by hallowed tales of witchcraft. The landscape, a patchwork of dotted farmsteads with hues of various shades, revealed crop growth. Small cultivated young forests rested on the slopes, with steep paths made by the continual treading of hikers endeavouring to reach the summit.

The land that laced the edge of the gardens on the right side of Harold Avenue was known, for no apparent reason, as 'Tilly's fields'. This offered a wonderland of nature for youngsters to hide, play and seek in. Here were found fresh air and freedom in abundance, which was a far cry from the claustrophobic mood of school. It was always saturated by children at weekends and holidays.

Granite-worn paths, and green, grassy clefts, made dangerous footing leading to a meandering brook. The water started wide and still, and gave off a stagnant odour, but children were willing to risk punishment of a soaking, by precariously slipping and sliding across mossy stepping stones. So often, shoes, socks and underwear had to be rung out and dried, after one young nipper would slyly push the one in front. It was always much safer to be last!

Stoops Estate became the saviour of Burnley's slum clearance. These modern semi-detached houses with gardens, replaced overcrowded and squalid back street properties, whilst offering healthier living. In 1929 Mr. and Mrs. Trickett Senior became the first proud tenants of number 60 Harold Avenue. Two years later Philip Richard was born, being the sixth of the couple's surviving children. But family bliss was cut short by the untimely death of Julia Agnes, the mother and pillar of the family. A tragedian could not have written a sadder tale. She died of strangulation of the bowel in the summer of 1938 - a missed diagnosis, due to the doctor's ignorance.

Philip's upbringing was divided between his father and his three elder sisters, Agnes, Winifred and Frances. As the years passed, Philip's brothers and sisters courted and married, leaving their father at home with Philip and the youngest child Thomas. Time had marched on, Philip and Thomas were no longer boys, but young men serving in the British Army. On her marriage to Philip in 1951, Audrey joined the Trickett family home, and the strict Catholic values Mr. Trickett harboured within it.

Occupying a corner plot, the pebble-dashed house commanded attention, as it imposed on the dwellings around it, somehow giving it an air of superiority. The garden was huge and meadow-like, spreading itself around three sides of the house. It was the ideal haven for small children and creatures alike. This plot had a missing gate and railings, which enabled it to become an easy escape route for the children.

Audrey herself often felt trapped, and she too yearned for an escape route. She hadn't been born in Burnley like Philip, but was a native of Blandford in Dorset. Her mother had died just three weeks after giving birth to her, leaving the newly-born Audrey and her five-year old sister Daphne, in the *incapable* hands of their father Joe, who relished too much in the demon drink. Well into the grieving process he met Molly from Burnley who was on holiday in the South. Joe was smitten.

Soon they were married, and moved up North to Burnley with the two little girls, settling uncannily in Dorset Street, Rosegrove. Harmony was short-lived; there was disdain amongst the family as Molly rejected Audrey because she was of such resemblance to her mother. Although Molly had never met Dorothy Hunt, she was haunted by her ghost. Jealousy revealed what a monster she was, as she became an instrument of cruelty.

Joe, not having bonded with his youngest child, decided to send Audrey back to relatives in Blandford - like a parcel or unwanted gift. Being a man of low, or no principles, he left her under the charge of the guard at Rosegrove railway station while still a young girl of around four-years of age. Audrey learnt from early childhood that most things in her life would be temporary. She would suffer highs and lows, good times and bad times. Her world was like semaphore, swapping and changing; the love of her aunts, uncles and cousins was always under threat of evaporating.

War broke out, and like many thousands of other children she was evacuated in a northerly direction for her own safety. Night after night her dream was to dance in the cornfields, or hear the gush of the expansive sea in

Poole, Bournemouth or Weymouth. That dream came true for her eventually.

Joe being Joe, allowed cynicism to raise its ugly head and claimed his daughter back. She was now fourteen, and of an age to be working and contributing to the upkeep of him and her wicked stepmother, Molly. The family had now established themselves in Middlesex Avenue on the Palace House Council Estate.

Audrey soon sought solace within the Bolt residence across the road. Mrs. Bolt was the hallmark of motherhood, she offered Audrey warmth, shelter and understanding. Audrey grabbed it for all its worth, she settled down and met good girlfriends Sylvia Howarth and Mary Traynor. In the fullness of time Molly and Joe produced their own daughter, a raven-haired beauty they called Kathleen. She too swung in and out of Audrey's existence as regular as a pendulum.

One weekend in September 1950, Sylvia took it upon herself to find Audrey a mate. Being engaged to Tom, Sylvia thought it right and proper that with Philip and Audrey they could make an enjoyable foursome. She had a cunning plan.

"Oh, Aud, Tom's got a really good-looking mate, he's called Philip," said Sylvia. "How about coming out on the town with us?" she suggested.

"Oh, I don't know," Audrey replied, "what if I don't like him, I'll feel a right fool?" hoping Sylvia would carry on with her persuasion.

"Well, I'll tell you what, I've got a brilliant idea." The two seventeen-year olds plotted until the plan made good sense.

Tom and Philip were to catch the bus at Rosegrove and be seated near the platform, with Philip taking the window seat at the left hand side. The two girls would be ready to step onto the bus on Accrington Road, the third stop on its journey.

As the vehicle approached, Audrey could see Philip wasn't only good-looking as her friend had promised, but undeniably handsome. He had a head of the blackest wavy hair, doleful eyes and a strong jawbone. Audrey could just make out thickset shoulders in a dark double-breasted suit. The plan was that if Audrey did not like the look of her suitor, then the girls would let the bus go.

However Audrey could not believe her luck. "Oh, Sylvia, I didn't think he'd be that good-looking. Get on the bus quickly," Audrey shouted in a panic.

This was the start of a great love affair which was often warm and generous, but many times plunged into despair. Love intertwined like two balls of wool, often neat and tidy, but sometimes tangled and knotted. The courtship took a short cut to marriage. They were wed with the grace and blessings of family and friends in the tiny chapel of St. Augustine's, Rosegrove on the 7th July 1951. There was another short cut - Carole Anne was born on December 23rd 1951.

Almost ten years had passed since Audrey left her beloved Dorset, and not a day went by without yearning thoughts occupying her mind. Audrey's heart and soul were those of a homemaker, a nest builder, converting reclaimed materials to make life more comfortable for her family. Although life was frequently inconsistent, she'd been granted a talent for needlework, not so much tailoring, but an eye for spotting pretty fabrics which she would use to enhance the clothes in which she clothed her children.

The Church's doctrine was that each child in their seventh year was to be blessed with the Holy Eucharist - their First Holy Communion Day. The requirement was to practice the faith by attending Holy Mass on Sundays and Holy Days of Obligation. As a sign of reverence to God, the girls wore a white dress, a wreath and veil, white ankle socks with matching footwear. The boys wore grey short trousers with a white, long-sleeved shirt and a red tie, grey socks, and black or brown shoes or sandals. This completed the children's outfits, and come what may, money or no money, all the children were somehow miraculously well turned out, as befitted such a solemn occasion!

Carole Anne being the first-born was due to receive the Sacrament in May. Despite plenty of notice having been given to all the families, Audrey was filled with worry, money was short, but this wasn't anything unusual. After searching the market-place in Burnley town centre, Audrey eventually found the fabric needed to produce the bride-like image she had in her mind's eye, for Carole Anne. It would be a long and tedious task, as the dress and underskirt were both to be made with loving care by hand. The material Audrey had chosen was called paper nylon, this was used for the underskirt; the fabric was as stiff as cardboard, and made her fingers so raw that they bled. The dress itself was pristine white bubble nylon.

To Carole Anne it resembled sago pudding, but she dare not let her mum know what she thought. Her veil of fine net was supported by a band of organza rosebuds framing her blonde bob of hair, and the whole presented a picture of angelic innocence.

Audrey was proud but exhausted by her hard work, but Philip promised that she would never have to sew by hand again. He proposed buying her an electric sewing machine, which they bought on hire purchase. Still it was a wise move. It took providence, for once the machine, called 'A Brother', had arrived, and Audrey had mastered the technology of such a futuristic piece of machinery, there was simply no stopping her. She took great pleasure in making her sons play-shirts, pyjamas and shorts. The girls wore dresses, always alike, baby doll night-wear and petticoats. The garments Audrey created were never perfect, but always beautiful.

Pregnancy beseeched Audrey yet again. Philip arrived home tired and aching from his steel-fixing job late one cold October evening, only to find his wife dragging herself around the house in tears.

"What's up with you," he asked.

"Oh! I don't know how to tell you," she said dolefully, barely able to face him.

When he did catch a glimpse, it was obvious how fraught she felt, her face, which was a near perfect profile, was now red and swollen.

"Well what the bloody hell **is** up with you? Come on," Philip shouted without much patience.

Audrey snivelled before replying "I'm off again."

"What the flaming hell do you mean? You bloody can't be; I'll tell you what it's a bloody curse I only have to throw my pants over the bed-end and you're bloody off again."

"Well I am," Audrey continued still weeping. "I've been to the doctor this morning and he's sure I am." She paused for breath before announcing, "And I'll tell you what Phil, I'm going to see about being sterilised after this." She spoke as though granting herself a promise.

"Don't talk daft," Phil argued back, "bloody sterilised, you can't, we're Catholic, they won't allow that."

Audrey meant what she said, and continued in the same vein whilst the tears carried on rolling down her cheeks. "The next time I go to confession, I'm going to speak to Father Corker. It's not him who has to keep the flaming kids."

The night settled, but Audrey's frustrations and discontentment came to the fore. Row after row became their pattern. Philip took his pleasure in drinking in the many public houses along Accrington Road on too many occasions. Drink turned him into a stupefied bully, causing mayhem day or night. The family's nerves were severed and on edge whenever he was in this appalling state.

Audrey found herself solitary and lonesome, wishing for what might have been had she not been uprooted from her birthplace. She longed for her mother, whose face was just an image. Marriage to Philip hadn't been continually blissfully happy. Everything seemed temporary or inconsistent. If work was plentiful, and he wasn't rained off from his outside job to idle days away in the pub, they were content, but too many times Audrey's energies were spent looking back. Unable to cope she'd talk to herself muttering curses, making plans, dreaming dreams, without realising the consequences all of this placed on her children.

In a droned voice she'd say, "If I was a bird I'd fly far, far away."

Being very sensitive, Carole Anne began to probe into the meaning of this often heard statement. It didn't baffle her, but it did worry her. She picked up vibes of sadness, and even of despair, watching her mum aimlessly chain-smoking. No longer did she derive pleasure from her pastimes of knitting and sewing.

It was the 17th October and Stephen's birthday; he'd been given a bus conductor's outfit. It was a time for make-believe. The settee had become the bus with its arm as the driver's seat. The little passengers sat in twos at the back of one another on the piece of furniture, transformed on the wings of imagination into a Corporation double-decker bus from the depot. It could have been an ark, with animals paired two by two. Stephen, being the birthday boy, was the bus conductor, with a little plastic, silver-coloured ticket machine strapped over his green checked shirt to the left, and an imitation red leather pouch crossed over his right shoulder. A navy blue nebbed hat, trimmed with fine red piping, crowned his glorious head of pale brown curls. Both Christine Mary and Stephen had inherited their father's locks, giving them the looks of cherubs, which truly delighted everyone they met.

The birthday boy marched down the bus shouting, "Fares please," in an equally angelic voice.

Each child handed him the correct amount of 'buttons' in payment, and gratefully received a ticket in return. The game was at its height when squabbling amongst the children broke out.

Cries of, "I want to be the conductor next," rose in the air.

"No, I am, it's not fair, it's my turn," shouted all the children in unison.

This penetrated Audrey's ears, "Right that's it, I'm sick of listening to this, I'm going." She sprang from the Marquette armchair sharply, wrapping herself in her long slack coat and uttered the well known words, "If I were a bird I'd fly far, far away." Then she was gone.

The game now over the children sat crying, but still blaming each other. It seemed like an age before she returned, cooler, calmer but unapologetic. The children felt oppressed and worried when their mother's moods took her to such lows. It could happen in the middle of summer, when warm outside, but it somehow always served to make it feel like winter. Equally though, she could cheer the darkest night with her high-pitched laughter.

They say opposites attract, and some such couples are loving and compatible, complementing each other's personality. Maybe this was too much to wish for with Audrey and Philip. They certainly looked handsome together, but their characters were so different. The children were split exactly down the middle, with two pessimistic and two optimistic. Two were influenced by their father's 'happy-go-lucky' attitude to life.

Christine Mary was a pleasurable child whom childless couples sought to borrow, to take her for days out. She was idyllic, and many a couple's dream child. At four-years of age, Stuart was the youngest. He had the personality of a comedian. His speech and manner captured any audience, even a following, thus ensuring his popularity. His milky, silk blond hair and chocolate brown eyes, were enough to melt the most unyielding of hearts. He was a recipe for the cutest of little boys. Carole Anne and Stephen were quite contrary to the light-hearted ones, they clung to their mother like suckling babies.

Chapter Two

Margaret exuded curiosity within her personality. Her glossy auburn hair was always washed and brushed, and sat in a neat shoulder-length bob, taken back from her face with a co-ordinated ribbon, to enhance her beautiful deep brown eyes. It was her eyes that silently asked the questions - she didn't need to be vocal. She could entice your inner thoughts from you with a simple smile. Even from the tender age of four, Margaret, who was a happy and contented child, was always willing and eager to bring new people into her home and her life.

Her parents, Alice and Leonard, devoted their lives to their only daughter's happiness. Both encouraged and welcomed her new-found playmates. This little girl's appetite for friendship was her trademark throughout her life, and made lasting impressions on the many people she came in contact with.

Christine, as she was now known, (for both sisters' names had now been simplified to plain Christine and Carole) absorbed school like a sunflower reaching for the sun and rain. She had a clever brain, and being articulate was eager to mix with her peers; she was so full of confidence. She was the perfect partner for Margaret. Christine was attracted to this well-groomed inquisitive new girl in school, and made it her mission to become her friend.

There was one striking difference in appearance between these two girls; this was their clothes. Margaret had an abundance of new clothes, whereas, although Christine's were made with loving care by her mother, there wasn't enough for a different frock every day, so any hand-me-downs from the neighbours were always greatly appreciated. This interest and difference between the two girls was the beginning of a long-standing friendship.

Playtimes were spent together in the school yard. Under the moon and over the stars was the game enjoyed by the majority of the girls, and even some of the boys. The only equipment needed was a long piece of skipping rope, and two children to twine it round at either end. Nimble feet and a vivid imagination ensured you stayed in the game. Some rope games were played in pairs, and Christine and Margaret made a winning team, much to the annoyance of Geraldine Holsworth who was full of competitive envy, which she openly displayed.

Often the two companions strayed away from the group of other children in the playground, and could be seen in tandem sharing secrets. Their friendship deepened, and much to Christine's delight she was invited to number 1, Paisley Street for Sunday tea.

Knowing exactly where Paisley Street was, as Christine had pre-empted this event several times in her dreams, there would be no need for her to persuade her mum to take her there, as this request would be met with a definite 'NO' anyhow.

Sure enough Christine ran the mile and half home from school that day, and both Carole and young Stephen had to keep pace with her.

Once home the words were out, "Mum guess what? I've been asked to tea at Margaret Hand's house on Sunday. Can I go? I know where she lives," Christine asked eagerly.

"Oh, I don't know, what about our Carole," her mum replied, as though the two sisters were joined as one.

"Oh please, please, she can't come *everywhere,"* Christine harped on and on.

Audrey shouted back in aggravation, "We'll see."

We'll see, when it was the answer to most questions, usually meant yes, but Christine was left with a dangling carrot, until her dad arrived home from the building site where he was working.

Carole's pessimistic streak left her sullen and unresponsive, with a permanently sad face that always needed coaxing into a smile. She didn't realise she looked unhappy for she wasn't old enough. She sat hunched-shoulldered on the silver metal plate attached to the black fire range, just staring with a blank expression, wondering why *she* hadn't been asked out to tea? Sometimes she curled so near the fire she felt like a restful cat, absorbing the warmth. This was where she felt most comfortable.

Her sister was hovering about charged through with excitement waiting for her dad to come home. As soon as he walked through the door she jumped around.

"Dad canna I go…" Christine was suddenly stopped short from asking her question by her father interrupting her.

"Bloody hell, let me get through the door," he yelled in a sharp, yet tired voice.

"Go to Margaret Hand's for tea on Sunday," she completed her question.

"I suppose so," he answered.

It was all Christine needed to hear; she danced around the room with glee, then lay back on the floor, arms bent at the elbow, with her hands supporting her head, now filled with dreams.

Carole sat ponderous, giving a slight upwards glance, before dropping her head to watch the rhythm of the vivid flames which danced in the fire-grate. Its radiation and warmth would hopefully divert her thoughts elsewhere.

Sunday did not require any announcing. It was a day that Carole and Stephen relished because it wasn't a day for school. Christine enjoyed *every* day, but found herself wishing the time away until two o'clock finally arrived. As on each Sunday, Mass came first. Although there were four Trickett children, only the three eldest children attended the service. Audrey was too busy to escort them, having already kitted the threesome out in their 'Sunday Best' coats and berets for the girls, and short pants, blazer and a peaked cap for Stephen. Phil felt it was his privilege to lie in on the Sabbath. Stuart could never guarantee to behave himself, and so skipped the ordeal for another twelve months.

St. Mary Magdalene's Parish Church stood unassumingly at the top of Haslam Street, immediately before the school. Its dowdy outward appearance matched that of the school, so neither one paid each other any compliments. The church's stonework had not seen any sand-coloured newness for half a century. There were no church grounds, just cast-iron railings set two feet apart from the heavily hinged oak door. The door itself that had once been varnished to give a high gloss mellow-finish, now looked aged and dull. The long windows were plain-leaded and nonchalant.

At first glance one would believe the architect to be somewhat unimaginative, who had grown bored with his task in hand, for the outside seemed incongruous. The porch was dark and gloomy, but was lifted by the well-preserved woodwork which formed a partition. Clear glass gave worshippers their first glimpse of the nave, chancel and the aisles. The crucifix, with St. Mary Magdalene at its feet, behind the marble altar, depicted Christ's last agony, and inspired the realisation of his suffering to the congregation.

There wasn't a centre aisle, but one either side of the wooden pews, which reflected the labour of the church cleaners, (volunteers with time to spare) who individually offered their sacrifices to God. Smaller pews were lined up in front of Our Lady's altar on the right, and the Sacred Heart on the left.

Light oak confessional boxes were placed on either sides of the benches, with the pulpit, almighty and upright, half-way up the right-hand aisle. The choir and organist were housed upstairs at the back of the church in order to re-echo their strains. A large-faced clock ticked almost silently from the back wall beneath the singers, but above the seated congregation. The overall effect managed to accomplish redeeming glory.

By the time the Trickett children arrived, the Holdsworth's had already taken their pride of place on the front bench in the centre pews. After quickly genuflecting, Carole, Christine and Stephen seated themselves on the second row behind them. Geraldine, Rodney and Jenny were also dressed in their best, but impractical attire of straw hats. The girls' hats were trimmed with ribbons and artificial flowers, and on their hands they wore lace gloves for effect.

Geraldine placed the half crown she'd been given for the offertory collection on the bench rail. This was more for everyone else's benefit, including the priest. Her next move was to turn and give Christine a scornful glance, aware that she was the one who had been asked to Margaret's for Sunday tea. Geraldine had been to 1, Paisley Street many times, yet she felt threatened by this newly-found friendship. Her blood churned and boiled inside, she could not simmer the way she felt, but it was unjustified, at least at this stage, for Margaret just wanted to extend her friendship to wider circles, without obstruction or other loyalties.

Geraldine was outpaced by no other child in the class; she was a joy to teach. She was always compliant, which earned her the title of *'teacher's pet'*. She considered her classmates as rivals, and was indeed a springboard for competition. Naturally her talents did not make her the most popular girl in the class. Now she found herself having to also compete to keep her friendship with Margaret. Geraldine believed herself too noble to lose it to one from the poorest of families in the class, yet she knew she didn't possess the same characteristics which Christine held. Life felt like something to strive for.

Father Corker, a short man seeking power, bellowed from the pulpit. Before his teachings he lectured to the listeners about the difficulties of carrying bags of coppers to the bank.

Carole and Christine simultaneously fingered their halfpenny piece in their pockets. This was all that their mum and dad could afford to spare for the church. They both decided that they should help him out here by keeping the money for themselves; they would get something from the halfpenny tray at Maguire's shop on the way home. Geraldine and her siblings smiled in unison as they placed their generous offerings into the collection plate.

Once outside church Christine skirted around looking for her friend. She'd spotted her in church standing at the back with her dad. He was a mature, lean gentleman, dressed in a smart overcoat and trilby hat. On his feet were the shiniest black boots any of them had ever clapped their eyes on. Carole thought he must have been a sergeant-major in the army, because she was sure they polished and shone their shoes at least once a day, even if they did not wear them.

The Trickett children made their presence known, and Mr. Hand responded his acknowledgement with a friendly nod, grin and a wink. Christine reiterated their arrangements for the afternoon, making sure it had not been cancelled.

With furrowed brows and drooping lips Geraldine spotted the opposition in conversation with Margaret and her father. The Holdsworth's family, if league tables were set in the parish, would have been positioned third, or possibly fourth from the top by means of finance. Their father being high up in management with a local firm, was able to provide a comfortable lifestyle for his wife and children. They enjoyed ballroom dancing lessons, ballet lessons for the girls, and all the finery that is essential when one is involved in such hobbies. Indeed nothing seemed to be beyond their means, yet Geraldine never appeared satisfied.

For Christine this day was becoming even more special, because her mum had finished the dress she was making for her, and had agreed that she could wear it to visit Margaret. It served to make the little girl look even more cherub-like. It was made of white cotton with teddy bears woven into the fabric. Instead of sleeves there was a simple frill around each armhole, with a gathered waist that was secured by a half-belt, fastening at the back. It fit her perfectly, although Christine thought that so it should considering the number of times she had to stand on the pouffe whilst Audrey placed pins precariously around her. The outfit was completed with white ankle socks and clear plastic sandals.

The long pull up Cog Lane seemed to take three times longer than usual, even though Christine encouraged her sister and brother to quicken their pace. Two o'clock finally arrived and Carole was asked to put her coat on and walk Christine part of the way to Paisley Street. This wounded her even more, but she did not protest. Dad had gone for a drink on Accrington Road, so Audrey insisted that Carole walk her sister as far as Cog Lane, then watch her over the recreation ground, otherwise known to all as the rec. Christine only had to walk along Dunoon Street, then turn left into Paisley Street, and Margaret's house was roughly twenty yards at the bottom.

Having left her sister out of sight, Carole wandered back along Harold Avenue, the route they had just taken, and she admired the awesome view across the horizon towards Pendle Hill. It was a clear afternoon, cool and not really one for dawdling, however she could not help but be struck by its beauty and elegance. A small white farmhouse stood lonely in the distance. Lonely, but for a single spreading tree. Carole imagined an elderly lady clad in a flowery, waist-apron standing at its gate.

"One day I'll visit that place," she told herself silently. As she moved along she studied how she would get there, having no idea, as there were no obvious paths to be seen, although a great deal of land stood between her and the white painted house beyond.

She had reached home and she already missed her sister, not too much in an envious way, but because they were rarely separated. They were like salt and pepper, strawberries and cream - always together.

Christine found her way to 1, Paisley Street, knowing even before she reached it that she wouldn't be met by broken railings, and that Margaret would not play out in a garden which would hinder her security with a broken gate. However she was most certainly not prepared for the enchanted garden that greeted her, for that's what it was, so perfectly enchanting. On the green-painted wooden gate was a little plaque stating in large letters.

'PLEASE CLOSE THE GATE'.

A fortress of trained privets standing over six feet high kept the garden secluded. These were guarding the flowers, and were even and trimmed razor-sharp. Paisley Street was part of the Hargher Clough Council Estate, offering modern dwellings with good sanitation to the folks of Burnley. The houses on the right hand side of the street were elevated, with four or five steps leading to the front doors, but no other possessed an entrance like Margaret's.

Christine tentatively walked down the path which had a border of the yellowest marigolds she had ever seen. She had of course seen marigolds in the garden next to her own house, but they were scattered, unlike the ones here. She revelled in the sight and smell of the budding roses that were cultivated in the garden. The most charming thing, was the way the roses intertwined together, forming an arch over the little path, as the wooden trellis welcomed its visitors. An array of greenery, not yet blossomed, stretched out to meet at the highest point of the structure, like friends holding hands in kinship. The whole scene seemed like something out of a picture book.

The letter-box and doorknob were brass, and had been rubbed to reveal their natural yellow beauty. An image of Geraldine's disapproval became the focus of Christine's thoughts, she felt like a cuckoo raiding another bird's nest, stealing grubs from the young. It didn't finish there, because before Christine could knock on the door, she could hear Margaret playing two balls on the wall to the side of the house.

"One, two, three O'Leary," the singing continued.

A little disappointed at not being able to use the shimmering door-knocker, Christine walked round towards the side of the house and was greeted excitingly by Margaret, who was playing ball just waiting to pass the time on until her friend arrived. Margaret shared Christine's enthusiasm at coming here for tea, because it sealed their friendship, to show that they had chosen each other to be special friends outside of school.

Leonard, or Mr. Hand as he was known, was in the back garden. He wore a brown smock over his shirt and tie as it was Sunday. He looked up at the small visitor, gave her a welcome smile saying, "Hello lovey." He was standing in the middle of a huge rhubarb patch.

Mr. Hand told Christine that he would pick some for her to take back home, but she was gently warned never to pick any herself, for his garden was his pride and joy, and his sanctuary.

Still amazed, Christine wondered if she should get a closer look at his built-up shoe. Having noticed it at church she wondered if his slippers would be the same? With this thought going through her head she realised that Mrs. Hand, Margaret's mum, was asking if she would like a glass of milk? Christine just nodded.

This large, brown-haired, bespectacled lady spoke with an unfamiliar accent; Christine later learnt that her friend's mum had been born in Wigan, about forty miles away, where her elderly mother - Margaret's granny lived, but was invited to stay over at Burnley most weekends.

Margaret took her pal into the house, firstly to the kitchen, which smelt delicious, like Gerry's bakery on Accrington Road, where the Trickett children sometimes had to go for their dad's bread. The other aroma which filled her nostrils, Christine hoped was her tea. Mrs. Hand was a cook at a local secondary school, so her expertise was based in the kitchen.

There was a yellow and cream kitchenette, just like the one Christine's Auntie Flo had. She wasn't her true auntie, but her adopted one, even her mum and dad called her their Auntie Flo. Her kitchenette was green and cream, but otherwise it was exactly the same as Mrs. Hand's.

From the kitchen Christine found herself in a large, square hallway, which held the curved stairway and the front door, which gleamed just as much inside the house as it did on the outside. Margaret's house contained a three-piece bathroom suite, unlike the one at Christine's home which only housed a bath and toilet. A little wooden cabinet was tucked into the corner and held luxury toiletries. On opening the door there was a strong smell of Dettol.

The front room had a small settee, which would only seat two adults. There were two armchairs opposite each other, these being reserved for Mr. and Mrs. Hand, and a highly polished table nearby was accompanied by four gleaming high-backed stand chairs. Christine wondered whose job it was to keep all this beautiful furniture shiny and elegant?

The fireplace was tiled with different shades of light brown, whilst on the mantelpiece stood four brass jugs, which could not have been rubbed any more to improve their gleam. They sent sunbeams across the room, which bounced back and forth off a mirror, to the window, to reflect in the glass of the black-framed picture, which dominated the room. It was a huge painting of the Last Supper; it was in fact as big as the one in the junior school hall. It hung from a heavy silver-coloured chain on the wooden picture rail.

The fire-grate was laid ready for when it got cold. Mr. Hand's chair was facing the glass bow-fronted cabinet, which housed an array of porcelain and china ornaments. At this point Christine thought that she couldn't possibly look and admire them, because it would take far too long and demand too much attention; she felt certain she would see them another day. There seemed to be more important things for her take in, like the wooden, arched Westminster clock. This too was just like the one which Auntie Flo had, which chimed every half-hour and on the hour, as it counted the time. This had turned her attention away from the cabinet as it chimed half past two.

Looking out of the window, Christine now saw Mr. Hand cutting her rhubarb; she hoped that there would be enough for her mum to make a pie, or a rhubarb crumble. Sometimes the children just ate rhubarb dipped in sugar. Christine asked Margaret if she could look at her bedroom?

Margaret led Christine upstairs explaining that they could not go into her mum and dad's room, because she wasn't allowed to do so. Christine just soaked up all the atmosphere surrounding her. They stepped into Margaret's bedroom and Christine thought it would be both strange and yet exciting to sleep by yourself. Margaret said she liked having plenty of room in her bed, but she sometimes put her 'old bear' in with her because she felt alone. She said it must be great sharing your bed like Christine did, but her friend thought otherwise. At least Margaret's bed had a silky flowered eiderdown on it, and not an old army coat like theirs did.

Whilst Mr. Hand had his rest, and his wife busied away in the kitchen, the two girls settled themselves on the widest step on the staircase. This was half-way up, where the rest of the steps turned the corner. Here they played with Margaret's dolls, dressing and undressing them, as they appeared to have far too many outfits for so few dolls. Margaret said that her Granny had knitted them before she had become unwell.

A soft voice called to say that the tea was ready, which interrupted the make-believe world that Margaret and Christine had hopped into. Whilst they awaited tea the little visitor searched around the room for something new to investigate. She could feel Mr. Hand's eyes penetrating through her back, but when she turned round to meet his gaze, she relaxed, as she was met with a smile and a twinkling eye.

She savoured the scene. The table was set with matching crockery, complemented by a little glass sugar bowl and milk jug. The cruet set added the finishing touch, ready for the forthcoming feast. And what a feast it was!

The food was delicious, meat slices, but the guest did not know what sort it was, but it didn't matter to her because it tasted so good. There were mashed, roast potatoes, carrots and cabbage. This was not the horrible cabbage which her mum cooked that tasted all wet. But even if she had thought it horrible, she felt sure she would still eat it, because she had noticed a spoon, which to her meant that there would be some pudding for those who cleared their plate. Margaret left some food on her plate, but it didn't seem to matter at this house, she was still served the best ever jam roly-poly and custard. Mrs. Hand poured everyone's tea, and Christine was even allowed to add milk and sugar for herself. It was a truly grand meal.

When it was time to clear the table Christine helped, then went into the kitchen realising she must have had beef for tea because there was still a huge piece of meat left on the side. She decided that it must have come from a cow to have been such a massive piece of meat in the first place.

Whilst Christine waited the few minutes before the clearing away could be completed, she found herself looking at the boots on Mr. Hand's feet. One of them had a false platform on it, which obviously meant even to someone young and inexperienced with life like herself, that one leg was shorter than the other. He did not seem to have any slippers; still she thought that she might ask Margaret about his foot at a later date as it intrigued her. She observed the rest of Mr. Hand discreetly; she feared that his hair had already lost its colour, and he was inhaling a pipe grasped to his mouth with one hand, whilst the other was tucked firmly into his smock pocket.

Her thoughts instantly tried to guess how old he was? He must be quite old she thought inwardly, because he didn't look anything like her dad. She decided that she liked this 'nice old man', but she wouldn't let Margaret know yet that she thought him old, because she might dislike it.

Whilst Christine soaked in the scene, she felt the warmth of the welcome she'd been given, and it put her in mind of a security blanket. Not a blanket all prickly and hairy like the ones on the beds at home, but one of softness and affection. Not a blanket wrapped tight and restricting to keep out the cold, but one that was loose, yet oozing freedom and reassurance, warmth and love.

This was one of the few times that washing up would have been a pleasure, but Margaret said that they would not be washing up because her mum always did it. It was lovely to think about washing all those nice delicate things, and looking deeper at the intricate patterns; still it was far better playing with Margaret on the stairs and landing.

Philip made his way home from the pub at 4:00 p.m.; this wasn't customary, but he knew that he had an errand to run later that evening. His daughter had to be collected from her schoolmate's house at seven. If he lingered longer in the Alma, staying like many others after time, he couldn't trust himself to be in any fit state to carry out his task. His arriving home relatively sober set Audrey aglow. Weekends could be a time of dread and fear because of his drunkenness.

Carole felt brave, she plucked up courage and asked if she could walk with him to collect her sister? She normally would have had to use tiny running steps to keep up with her dad's giant strides, but today she ran and skipped in front, twirling and dancing along the way.

Time went too fast, and Christine heard the door-knocker sound. It wasn't Margaret who opened the door, even though the two girls were playing near it, but Mr. Hand, who greeted Philip with Carole by his side.

Mr. Hand paused from smoking his pipe and said, "Eh hello lad; you're Dickie Trickett's son aren't ya?"

"That's right," Philip answered in a wary sort of way, something always nagged him when he realised strangers knew him.

"I took a drink in the Clarion Club many a time with old Dickie. You've got some grand childer, I see 'em every week in church, but I don't see thee lad; anyway they don't misbehave, I keep an eye on 'em, you know." He didn't always use such a deep Lancashire dialect, but on this occasion it was used as a welcome gesture.

Mrs. Hand looked at Carole and said to Christine, "Is this your big sister? I wouldn't call her big, would you?"

In fact although Carole was the eldest of the three girls, she was the smallest.

Carole found her voice and nervously asked, "Can I come next time Mrs. Hand?"

"Course you can love," she replied in a high enthusiastic voice.

Carole did a bit of a jig on the spot.

"Right lasses," Philip said, "Christine thank Mr. and Mrs. Hand for tea, and tell Margaret you'll see her at school tomorrow the pair of you."

In chorus the girls diligently said their thank you and goodbyes.

All the way home Christine talked and talked of the delicious tea and the games that they had played. Carole just used her imagination, but that night they dreamed the same dreams.

The visit secured a wonderful friendship between the girls. They had bonded in a way that could only be severed by death, and even death would not be able to cut the umbilical cord. Margaret and Christine had become huckleberry friends for life.

Chapter Three

Audrey was now well into her fifth pregnancy, but the child she was carrying was in too much of a hurry. Elaine Margaret, (the second name chosen after one of the nurses) was born on Friday 4th March 1960. She was three month's premature and resembled a skinned rabbit. A christening ceremony was urgently conducted in the hospital, as her condition was considered life-threatening, but medical staff were hoping for a miracle. They didn't simply rely on prayer, but the power of medical equipment. A police escort brought an incubator from one of the big hospitals in Manchester.

In the early 1960's such technology was relatively new, and babies born at six month's gestation were given very low odds of survival. However doctors, nurses, Audrey and Philip had hope, and they clung steadfastly to it for three months, until the baby girl had gained enough weight to be allowed home.

For the Trickett children at home, an incubator was something of a mystery, but their dad sat them down and gave his version of such a contraption.

"Well, our new baby Elaine Margaret, has arrived too early. She is really very tiny, weighing just two pounds and eleven ounces, and is just a bit bigger than a bag of sugar. Because she is so small she feels the cold easily, and cannot keep herself warm properly. The doctors have got this 'gas oven' bed to help keep her body temperature right."

Part of his statement was correct, they *did* need to monitor her body temperature, but his children now had wild imaginings of what a 'gas oven' bed was like?

Stuart came out with the most obvious question, "Hey dad, do you mean they strike a match and light it underneath?"

"Will she not burn?" Stephen asked worriedly.

"No no! you daft ha'peth." Phil thought he was putting them right as he tried to explain, "you plug it in."

Well the youngsters only knew of Auntie Flo who had an electric oven, so all the talk of plugging in was very alarming to them. Soon however, the daily routine usage of the incubator set all their minds at ease.

Elaine eventually thrived and blossomed like a delicate summer flower. The little skinned rabbit who was born red, transparent and raw-looking, was now transformed into a walking miracle, and the family's prayers had been answered.

Philip doted on his little girl, for she had stirred something inside him that he had never felt before. This was fear, not physical fear, for he was a hard man and was frightened of nobody. In fact in his youth he had earned himself a title, *'The cock of Accy Road'*. In other words, no one dared mess with him! But this was more a deep *emotional fear*, something he could not recall having ever encountered before. For three months he had lived on nervous energy, in the shadows of despair, now he exuded paternal pride and joy.

For a short time a truce was called from the drunken brawls and domestic arguments that were eroding his marriage. For the children it was a time of family bliss, and such perfect joy that they wanted so much to scoop it up and save it in their pockets, then they would be able to bring it out to their rescue in moments of torment, for sadly they already knew from past experiences, that all this harmony would be short-lived.

Just weeks after Elaine had been discharged from the Special Care Baby Unit, Audrey was rushed into the Surgical Ward with severe appendicitis. A nervous breakdown followed, and all the monstrous medical intervention that came with it, such as electric shock treatment and being doped up with tablets.

Carole and Christine soon became surrogate mothers to their siblings, and were quickly plunged from childhood to premature maturity. The warning signs had always been there, but there was no one to help or take heed.

Carole saw her fate as an escape route from school. She had been separated from her younger sister in school for years now, but had never really adjusted. She was too much of a worrier to relax and enjoy childhood pleasures, and the discovery of learning. She envied the clever children, and often sat day-dreaming, wondering what it would be like to be in their shoes? However this was not at all the way forward for Carole to grow more confident and gain an education. She readily volunteered to look after the home, her mother, even the new baby.

As a result she became more withdrawn, turning into a plodder, struggling to keep pace with her peers at school. Once she had plummeted to such depths, she could not find a hoist to help her rise back up.

On the other hand, Christine took to her new role with contempt. She felt trapped and caught in a snare. She loved school and would not miss one day. No one, but no one was going to steal *her* education and *her* flowery days of innocence.

Miss Duckworth, a young, dark-haired schoolmistress brought tyranny to the classroom. Her looks were so deceptive. Being slim, she was able to wear figure-hugging skirts of varying patterns and textures, with matching lambswool crew neck sweaters. High heeled court shoes complemented her shapely legs, as well as giving her added height. She insisted on testing her pupils' mental arithmetic skills constantly. Children who did not gain more than seven out of ten correct answers, received one stroke of the cane for each incorrect response.

"Right Miss Trickett, how many have you got right?" Miss Duckworth enquired smarmily.

"Six Miss," Carole replied, both quietly and timidly.

Miss Duckworth's voice was loud and shrill, "Stretch out your arm girl, and do not move it!" She emphasised each first letter deliberately.

The teacher swung the cane with gusto, whilst her face creased with pleasure at the whistling sound the stick made.

Carole's face grimaced in pain, whilst her stomach curdled.

Solace was sought the following week at Margaret's house. The two girls set off across the rec. at the usual time of 2:00 p.m. Through the gate of the enchanted garden, the gleaming letter-box invited them to knock, and the door was opened. Christine recognised the smell of good wholesome food, which would be for their Sunday tea. After the customary glass of milk the playmates decided to play make-belief on the stairs. The girls set up house on the stairway, with each step becoming individual beds.

Carole could not help but be inspired by the gleaming cleanliness of it all. As sure as there are seven days in a week the paintwork was washed in warm sudsy water. The dark wool carpet was brushed, until its texture imitated the tight curls of a curly perm. It was then secured with triangular-shaped varnished rods on every step.

Just before dinner Granny asked if the girls would like to set the table? There would be two sittings because of the two extra guests. The Trickett girls had never actually set a table before and were a little confused, but Granny soon put them at ease as she taught them the rules of place-setting. The youngsters were served their food first. This consisted of a warming roast dinner of meat, healthy vegetables, potatoes and lashings of thick gravy sauce.

Christine gave her sister a nudge, together with her acknowledgement of, "I told you so."

Carole now realised why Margaret was not as small as the Trickett children. Margaret's Granny didn't match the rest of her family somehow. She was small and frail, with her backbone rounded at the shoulder. Her hair was metallic grey, tied in a tiny bun in the nape of her neck.

An apron around her waist was evidence that she had come prepared to help.

Mrs. Hand did not resemble her mother at all, for she was tallish, and plump. She wasn't typically young either, nor was her outfit of the latest fashion. She wore a practical and demure long pleated skirt, teamed with a neat silk blouse.

The meal finished and enjoyed, both Carole and Christine showed natural politeness by asking in unison, "Please may we leave the table?" in appreciative voices. This was something which they always had to do at home, even though they stood around the table for their meals at Harold Avenue.

Mr. Hand rose from his chair, removed his pipe - which seemed to be a permanent fixture, and waved his hand to beckon the children to go and play.

Mrs. Hand warmed to the Trickett girls; she admired their impeccable manners. A thought passed through her mind that although they had little, they had the breeding of the gentry. 6:45 p.m. arrived, and it was time for them to make their way back home to Harold Avenue.

Mrs. Hand was heard to say, "I haven't got one daughter, I now have three!"

Margaret and her mum walked with them as far as the rec.

As they waved she shouted with concern in her voice, "Go straight home now, don't tarry."

Chapter Four

Christine and Margaret were now of an age to be taught by the indignant Miss Duckworth, who still used the same tactical measures for weeding out the disadvantaged and slower children.

Geraldine Holdsworth had two advantages, she was one of the brightest girls in the class, and her social background freed her from the harm of corporal punishment. Margaret also had nothing to fear, because her father was well respected by the church. Christine was clever, she always gave Miss Duckworth the results she craved, and therefore managed to escape her teacher's wrath, but all three were witnesses to the vile punishment dished out daily to those less fortunate.

At the start of the school term, St. Mary Magdalene's had seen an influx of Italian immigrants settling within the parish. A young boy, speaking and understanding barely enough English to get by on, sat next to Christine for lessons. She was bemused by him, liking the way Ricardo wore his shorts, shorter than short!

Having very little patience, Miss Duckworth wasted no time in showing the poor boy the purpose of the cane. Every day he joined the line to receive thrashes for each sum he got wrong.

One day Christine could not stand this any longer, as pity for Ricardo got the better of her. As soon as the maths test commenced, Miss Duckworth was pacing in a sort of goose-step, firing out questions. Christine slipped her paper to the middle of the desk, then gave Ricardo a gentle tap and a smile with a downward glance, so that he understood to copy her answers.

The test was completed, and Miss Duckworth in her shrill and demanding voice said, "Right all those with ten out of ten, raise your hands." Her eyes did not leave the wooden floor for a while, for she knew all her clever pupils well.

Ricardo threw his hand into the air with pride. He felt that someone high above him had a piece of string attached to the tips of all of his fingers, and was stretching and pulling them upwards.

Miss Duckworth glanced at her pupils, then shouted far more piercingly than ever before, "Ricardo Benito, get out here, and bring your work with you."

He hesitated, not exactly sure just what this teacher wanted. Then he did as ordered.

"This cannot possibly be your *own* work," she screeched.

There was sympathy in Christine's eyes as she watched her friend receive ten strokes, one for each sum. Ricardo sat nursing and squeezing his hands for the rest of the lesson, wiping away his tears on the sleeve of his fine-knit Italian sweater. Christine's throat became tight and swollen as she gulped, for she too wanted to cry for her neighbour. She tried in vain to help her little Italian friend whom she liked immensely, as he was so bright and cheery most of the time. At this moment though, she felt a mixture of emotions battling within each other, to reach the brim and overflow. These ranged from sympathy and anger, through to frustration, but disbelief and numbness reflected most in her eyes.

Looking at the windows and the frosted glass partitions separating each classroom, she thought this school was like a concentration camp. Only a morsel of natural light found its way into the room. The door was tightly shut, and all thirty children were hemmed in a big square box-like room, with no possible means of escape.

Ricardo had let his mind drift back to his homeland, where adults were child-loving. Italian parents cherished their bambini, and were not afraid to show this adoration. This tyrant's deplorable behaviour would not have prevailed where **he** came from, for Miss Duckworth would not have survived.

As previously hinted, life in the Trickett household was not consistent. One of the main events in the life of a Roman Catholic child was the day the child received the Sacrament of the Holy Ghost - their Confirmation. Preparation in school went on for several months, as every child had to be able to recite the catechism. If this knowledge was not achieved in time, then the child had to wait for a further four years, as this sacrament was pronounced by the Bishop himself, who only visited every fourth year. The pupils worked hard and long to make sure that they knew the contents of their catechism.

Father Corker came into the class, and randomly selected some child to quote a selected phrase, and woe betide anyone who stumbled under the pressure.

On the practical side, no preparations had been undertaken at home, owing to Audrey's mood swings and depression, as she was now very affected by the mixture of antidepressants and sleeping tablets she took.

Christine had outgrown her first Holy Communion dress. The veil she had used then, had belonged to Carole, who would need it herself, as she too was to be confirmed.

Christine was told, "You will just have to borrow an outfit."

Exactly where she could obtain one from, had as yet not been thought of. Four classes of children would be receiving the Sacrament of Confirmation that special Sunday afternoon, therefore the likelihood of being able to borrow one was minimal. She knew that she could have the loan of a wreath and veil from school, but by now all the better ones had already been chosen.

Mrs. Hargrove, the sewing teacher, prattled on and on as to how special the day would be for the 'young brides' of Christ. It was more than Christine could take to say that nothing had been done at home, so she simply ignored the situation, hoping her mum might come too a bit, and quickly make her a white dress, and buy her a veil.

In desperation, only a few days before the big event, Christine managed to linger in the classroom after the lesson, and confide in Mrs. Hargrove. She explained to the teacher that her mum said that she should borrow an outfit, but so far she had not found anyone who could lend her the required attire.

The teacher, being a compassionate person, felt quite touched and saddened by Christine's plight, and offered the child reassurance by telling her not to worry about it. The poor girl wondered if she should have told Mrs. Hargrove sooner, with her being the sewing teacher, she might have made her one. Still she would have needed the material, so maybe that wasn't a good idea after all.

When Mrs. Hargrove got home from school that day, one of the first things she did was to wash and press her *own* daughter's confirmation dress, which had been lovingly packed away in tissue paper after its use. Now she had it ready to take to school for her pupil. Mrs. Hargrove's daughter Clara attended a different school, and so no longer needed the dress.

It was Friday, and as Christine walked to school she told her sister that she had confided to her teacher that she did not have a white dress for the confirmation. Carole herself had been worrying her socks off over the dilemma.

Mrs. Hargrove sent one of the children from her class to find Christine at playtime, to give her the confirmation dress. The child was dumb-struck when she tried on this beautiful white gown. It was perfect! The size, the fit, everything looked just right, and Christine was such a pretty girl, that the slightly discoloured wreath and veil would hardly be noticed on her. She shone like a ray of sunlight.

She just beamed at Mrs. Hargrove and said, "Thank you Miss."

This alone was enough to bring tears to the eyes of this caring woman.

The month of March was not only recognised for winds, hare breeding, Mothering Sunday, Easter time (if the first moon appearing after equinox fell in this period) but in the ecclesiastical calendar, for March meant mid-Lent. This was a time of fasting, good deeds, sacrifices as offerings to God. Teachers and Clergy alike, spoke of 'sackcloth and ashes', but that, as the children understood, was for the 'olden times'.

The St. Joseph Penny Collection made its annual appearance in this season. This was a fund-raising mission on behalf of the diocese of Salford. Each child, or little missionary, was given a cream-coloured card, measuring about six by eight inches, with pennies amounting to one shilling printed on it, along with a straight pin. The idea being for every penny you donated, you had the privilege of sticking the straight pin into the paper cube, thus leaving a permanent pin mark. The top three children in the school who managed to fill their paper with the most pinpricks were invited to the Bishop's Palace for tea.

There were now four Trickett children attending St. Mary Mag's, as they had taken to abbreviating the full name of the school, like some of the 'bigger fish' in the juniors. They each met at the gate when school was over for the day, ready for the walk home; the younger two waving their bits of paper, and brimming over with excitement.

Carole and Christine soon dampened their younger siblings' spirits, making their laughter subside, as their own previous experiences had taught them that there was no way on God's earth that they would ever be invited to eat with the Bishop, for the same pupils were favoured year after year. They could name them now as Geraldine Holdsworth, Margaret Hand and Michael Flint.

Harold Avenue was a route march to and from the school, but the children always found as much variation as they could. If the weather was kind they would dawdle through the pens and seek adventure. An alternative route was straight down Cog Lane. They would then call for Paul Maguire, and Jimmy and Patrick Ellinsworth, who all lived on Cog Lane. Together this band of children would frighten the wits out of each other, with spooky stories of witches who lived in some of the foreboding looking houses which they passed. They told stories of the mad witch, clothed in a hat and cloak as black as coal, stirring children in her cauldron, until they were thoroughly cooked and good enough to eat. This tale usually served to put a sprint into everyone's step. They would suddenly find a surge of energy, quickening their journey considerably.

At other times they moved at a snail's pace, balancing on garden walls, ducking below windows, to avoid folk who sat minding their own business in their own living-rooms. Woe betide anyone who was slow enough to be caught.

Stuart had to hold someone's hand to walk across the stone walls. His impish legs were not yet long enough to jump from wall to wall across the paths, where often the garden gate was higher. He needed to be lifted, which meant the walk home could take almost an hour. When the other children joined their journey, it was guaranteed that all the children would be late for school, because they all became engrossed in each other's world of fairy tales and games. The journey home from school also often exceeded an hour, because the Trickett's would play at the Ellinsworth's house for a little while, usually until they were reminded by the rumbling in their bellies that it soon would be time for tea. Then they would bid farewell to everyone, and travel the rest of the journey faster.

Audrey never worried that her children were often so late home from school. When she was alert she consoled herself that they were all together, and would be in the midst of a game, simply having lost track of the time. She would have worried of course if there was one of the children missing, as they always went to and from school together.

Cog Lane had several inclines, and some of them were quite steep, and as sharply sloping as the small slippery slide in the playground. This made Stuart's dumpy legs ache, causing him to lag behind. He often demanded a donkey ride on the back of one of his sisters. He became bored as well as hungry, his mind catching glimpses of him having a posh tea with the Bishop in his Palace. Momentarily, he took his pin and paper and stabbed as many holes as he could in the small square card. He had not quite grasped that this meant he would have to find a lot of money, and that his mum, dad and teachers would not be very pleased with him. In fact he would probably get pasted when he got home.

Carole, acting in her motherly role, chastised him. His eyes moistened, then his tears flowed. She felt guilty and rather sad for her little brother; it was not fair, life itself was not fair, all he wished for was a trip out and a posh tea. Once home Audrey suggested that they knocked on the doors of the wealthier neighbours, some of whom were comfortably off.

Mr. and Mrs. Kent, who only had one grown-up daughter, had a car and a telephone, this made them **nearly** rich. Asking people outside the family was surely begging on the Church's behalf. The Kent's disapproved of this, and kept their money firmly in their pockets. By the same token the Church had introduced moral blackmail amongst the children. The two Trickett girls resented this, because it highlighted the ones who had very little, yet uplifted the ones who already had everything.

Carole and Christine had long since dismissed any thoughts of an outing to the Bishop's Palace. On Sunday the atmosphere at home had become unpleasant. Dad was out, and mum was in and out of a trance-like state, owing to the misuse of her antidepressant tablets. The sisters made their way over the rec. to Paisley Street, opened the gate, and walked down the path of the enchanted garden, before tapping on the door, hoping to play with their friend.

Mrs. Hand answered the door and was surprised to see the girls. She explained that Margaret was at the Bishop's Palace in Salford, where she was having tea. Regrettably, she did not ask them to come and wait for Margaret's return, instead she told them that they would probably see Margaret at school in the morning.

The two sisters plodded back down the path totally jaded with disappointment. They had no wish to return home yet, as they did not feel there was much to go home for. Neither Mrs. Hand nor Margaret had any idea of their home circumstances. Their mother's nervous breakdown had been their secret; they felt it too ruinous and shameful to be shared, and far too bewildering to be out in the open.

After aimlessly wandering around the nearby streets, the two girls sat themselves on the edge of the pavement, feeling very much deflated. They sat playing and messing in the silt, and melting gas tar with used lolly sticks; their heads were bowed low like poor banished children.

Suddenly, they rued not having made their way home, for just then Miss Fenn's silvery blue car pulled up a few feet away from them. Margaret and Geraldine alighted the vehicle together, acknowledging the girls as they made their way through the gate of the fairy tale garden. The Trickett girls were left sat nursing a whole avalanche of embarrassment.

Chapter Five

Nestled towards the left of 'Tilly's field', stood four rows of terraced houses, humble yet proud. These properties had originally been built to accommodate the men and their families, when they had moved from Cornwall to Burnley in search of work. This tightly-knit community became a settlement, that was known to the locals as Little Cornwall. In the late 1900's the Cornish tin mines had mostly dried up. Workers had travelled North, to work in equally dangerous conditions down the coal-mines.

Hapton Valley, or 'Happy Valley' as it was often referred to, was based on the foot edge of Hambledon Hill. The tall mechanical wheel was ever waiting and paying homage to the gallant men it served daily. It lowered them at great speed in the metal cage hundreds of yards beneath the earth's surface. Then it stood waiting patiently, to bring the workers safely back to inhale the fresh air at the end of their shift, and open their eyes to daylight. It became a characterised landmark bestowed upon the countryside.

Little Cornwall was built of stone, albeit that the houses were cold and dispiriting. You could almost smell the cold. Inside sanitation did not exist, and the damp rose up the inside walls, leaving green wavy lines. Generations had grown up and moved on, but Hapton Street, Valley Street and Griffin Street somehow survived, but appeared to be stuck in a time warp, unchanging with each passing year. Shoulder to shoulder folk braved the storms, generating the love of an extended family, with arms outstretched, and ever welcoming.

Valley Street and Griffin Street were open to the elements. Bearing the wind and rain with courage, they were rewarded with the light and warmth of the exposed sunshine. Two sides of Hapton Street ran down the inner middle, like a gully gaining shelter in the fall and winter, so the sun skipped over Hapton Street. On grey days her inhabitants could not be blamed for mistaking the darkness for an eclipse.

Cobblestones stretched both front and back, making treading them difficult when wet or frosty. Each dwelling had a backyard, secluded by a brick wall and a high wooden gate. Some were neat and tidy, whilst others were shabby, with fallen mortar left unswept on the concrete floors. One common denominator was a grey tin bath, which hung on a large nail on the external wall. There was an outside lavatory, which also had a nail hanging on the door, complete with a string holding last week's newspapers, cut out into squares for one's primitive personal hygienic purposes. These homes formed an abstract picture in the viewing distance of the tree-lined avenues of Stoops Estate, which outshone Little Cornwall.

Although the houses were old, and perhaps somewhat inadequate, they were not classified as slums; indeed some were rare, and could be described as little palaces. One such home was at 5, Griffin Street.

Kathleen Manning was the youngest occupant at this address, and was thought of as a model child by everyone who ever met her, with her gloriously thick ebony hair, brushed aside her pale, yet unblemished skin, then made into two plaits that were fastened with silk ribbons.

Carole and Christine were jointly in agreement that Kathleen reminded them of Dorothy - the young Kansas girl in the story of '*The Wizard of Oz*'. Her deep-set green eyes gave her the typical established features associated with the Irish.

From Kathleen's living-room window, nothing could be seen but a blank stone wall, darkened with age. This was the Ginny wall, known as the 'Ginny-Run'. The individual stones which made up this dismal wall had been counted both by Kathleen and other members of the household, over a thousand times, due to boredom, or when it rained too hard for the children to play outside. Showing disgust at the lack of a view, even if it was expected, they were often told how lucky they were to live in a house which was actually owned by their parents.

To Kathleen the view from the front bedroom was something else. The window was elevated high, and it was quite like opening a gilt-edged entrance to the natural world surrounding her. Kathleen's eyes scanned from left to right, as if following the rainbow for the pot of gold. In the far distance to the left, Hambledon Hill stood dark and daunting.

On the same side, but in the foreground, was Burnley Cemetery. This was not a dismal place; it could sometimes be eerie, but mostly simply exuded peace. As a sharp earthly reminder that we are all merely mortals, the granite gravestones, strong, mighty and upright, reflected the flashes of light from the sun, or beaming head-lamps of traffic. The burial ground was an adventurous place for some of the children who were allowed to stray further afield.

In its depths lay Bluebell Wood and the Rhododendron Wood, where the older boys and girls met. Some of the boys owned airguns and shot at the wild defenceless rabbits, whilst threatening younger children simply by the appearance of a gun. It was a sign for the younger children to keep away, denoting it as strictly teenage territory.

It was whilst surveying the structure of her rainbow, that the realisation dawned on Kathleen of how fortunate she was to live here in Little Cornwall, within a happy and contented family. Her parents, John and Kitty, were both natives of the Emerald Isle - Ireland. They had met purely by chance, in the unlikeliest place - London.

England was then at war with half the world, yet Kitty was drawn to the Capital City, like a straight pin to a magnet. She'd started life in County Cork in Southern Ireland, but sadly her mammy died of a malignant cancerous tumour when Kitty was barely into adulthood. Her strict Catholic father expected her to run the house, whilst simultaneously taking care of him and her younger sister. Aged just seventeen, Kitty felt the need to spread her wings, for she was a free spirit in search of happiness and freedom, as well as contentment.

As a teenager, Kitty's sister Constance, defied all the rules and regulations belonging to her father, the church and the Irish Catholic Society. So wayward was Connie's behaviour, that she found herself being quite literally dragged off to the Magdalana Convent.

The Magdalana homes were notoriously cruel, and were supposed to act as a deterrent for promiscuous girls. They were run strictly by nuns, with no other desire except to drive the devil from the girls who entered their convent. Local girls who found themselves in trouble, or whose parents simply could not afford to feed them, were sent there. The gossips said that some of the Irish colleens were institutionalised to the convent simply for just being too pretty! They implied that this was done in order to feed the sexual appetites of the priests, old and young alike; but whether there was any truth at all to the rumours we'll probably never know.

Kitty arrived in Tooting, North London, in the midst of 'The Blitz'. The bomb damage was unbelievable, and she found herself speaking out loud to herself. "Where on earth have I come to?" She even answered herself too, "But it is better than Cork," and she consoled herself with this.

She soon found good company with Mrs. O'Connor, who offered her full board and lodgings in return for work in the Shamrock café that she owned. Kitty's Irish roots had drawn her to this quaint, but busy little place. She liked the feel and the atmosphere which was streaming from the friendly crowd, who had sheltered there in the many days of desperation. They were mostly natives of Ireland, ex-patriots, looking for some sort of contact with home. Somehow they reminded her of the Gaelic tones of her lost family.

Yet she was never lonely when she was there, for the only person she really missed was her dead mammy. She longed to talk to her, to tell her of her new life in war-torn London. Many a time, instead of eating lunch in the café she would walk to the common, especially if it was raining. Kitty loved to walk in the rain. Feeling the damp on her face allowed her the freedom to cry openly, without embarrassment, as her tears mingled with the falling raindrops. This was her way of mourning her mammy. Sometimes she would stop and rest; her favourite place being a wooden bench stripped of its paint, but settled under an expanding chestnut tree. It was on one such occasion that she met John.

Today was not the first time John had seen this young girl. He had passed by her before, often just nodding as an acquaintance would, but each time he was disturbed by what he saw. He recognised grief, and he wondered why a lovely young girl was so troubled? Perhaps she had lost family in the air raids, after all so many people had lost their homes, their families and their lives.

John too had the blood of the Irish; he had lived in Dublin, the capital of Southern Ireland. He had left behind him, his parents and fourteen brothers and sisters. Work was hard to come by in Ireland, and John had a thirst for employment in order to better himself, and provide a home for his future family. He was overridden with guilt, having left the land and the people he loved.

John was a mild-mannered man, a gentleman in the truest sense. This good-looking fellow had often been seen in Dublin with a pretty girl on his arm. He had noticed a lightness, a softness in Kitty's eyes. He wanted to hand her a lifebelt, to give her buoyancy, but he was afraid that if he approached her, she would sink deeper into herself. In fact it was Kitty who made the first move by asking John if he knew what time it was, as her lunch break was almost over. John was pleasantly surprised by her familiar Irish drawl, and he answered in similar tones. The pools in Kitty's Irish eyes melted John, as they had struck a chord in his heart.

A loving courtship ended in the registry office just four months after their meeting. They married for better or for worse, as did many couples who met during the war, desperate to tie the knot. What was there to wait for? John knew as soon as their eyes met that Kitty was the girl for him. Neither of them yearned for many of life's extravagances, just to bring love and joy to each other and their future offspring. They had found contentment in its deepest form.

Married life for John and Kitty Manning was blissful, Kitty thought that she had gone to heaven. The only drawback was living in the crowded room above the Shamrock café. Oh it was clean and comfortable, but Kitty felt that she needed to live away from her place of work. It was stifling her, as Mrs. O'Connor, always seemed to need her on her days off.

It was about this time that John received a letter from an old aunt and uncle, who had uprooted from Dublin many years before the war. They had made their home in a modest two-bedroom house in the Duke Bar area of

Burnley. Exhaustibly long rows of terraced streets formed this thriving maze-like region to the North of the town, with many of the cotton mills being responsible for its success. The letter was an invitation for John to join his relatives, which John had pondered over to himself all day, before finally showing it to his wife.

Kitty climbed the stairs from her day's work. She was hot and clammy, having sweated all day in the steamy atmosphere. She just collapsed into the saggy armchair. Unusually John was already home, the sound of the kettle was almost whistling, which was a warm and cheery sound, which on its own brought a smile to Kitty's face.

"Eh, sit down lass, I've got something to show you," John said in a slightly quivering voice, unsure of his convictions.

This brought Kitty onto her feet, "What's wrong John," she asked nervously.

"There's nothing wrong love, just let me read this letter to you."

'Dear John,

How pleased your Uncle Pat and I were to hear you and your young lady had got yourselves married. We liked the picture you sent. Kitty looks a right bonny lass, and you look so suited to each other, but we worry about you John, down there with all those bombs going off. There's nothing like that up here, you know. They call Burnley the sleepy valley. The Germans can't find us as I've said before.

What it is John, me and your Uncle Pat have a lovely spare room. We'd love to have you and Kitty here with us. Think about it, you could make a new life up North, there's plenty of work at 'Butts and Dicks', the foundry. Talk it over with Kitty, and you take care of your two selves.

Love for now,
Auntie Maggie and Uncle Pat'.
XXX

John had wondered if Kitty would want to move on so soon, but in reality he too had worried about their future in this stricken place. The more thought he had given to his aunt's letter, the more excited he became; his aunt's cosy home in Burnley could be just the anchor they needed, a place where they could be moored and settled.

Kitty's full lips formed into a pleasing smile, for she too had niggling doubts dancing around in her mind. Not that they had felt unstable, but nothing was certain for any couple at the present time in London. They both knew that the time had come to be wise, and Kitty's tummy tickled in anticipation.

She clapped, danced and hugged John, all at the same time, "Let's do it, let's go John."

John grinned with relief, thinking to himself, "Great minds think alike," as the saying goes.

Kitty was more than willing to be encompassed within John's family, even to the extent of sharing their home.

Maggie and Pat were full of enamour, they felt young again, relieved from the doom. John was a good worker, and found a position at Butterworth's and Dickinson's, near Rosegrove, Burnley. Meanwhile Kitty, by the law of nature, found herself to be expecting their first baby. John's family were so kind and generous with their time and property, but women are habitual creatures, which left Kitty wanting to be on her own with John. She felt the need for nest building, to be in her own territory, to have privacy to talk, or to dream, and to make plans for their new family.

Her husband understood these feelings, as they communicated well and were aware of each other's needs. Consideration was the way they worked together. Cohabiting with relatives had enabled John and Kitty to save a little money, and one day John came home with all the paraphernalia from the Building Society about mortgages. Kitty was dismayed, she had her mind set on one of the lovely scheme houses which had been built, sprawling little communities in urban areas of the town. These were houses with bathrooms and indoor toilets, and gardens safe enough for children to play in. But these homes were rented and never possessing ownership, representing dead end money as John would say.

He had made a decision, and quite uncharacteristically dug his heels in. He knew that they could only stretch to a run-down place, with a deposit and a mortgage, but he had heard talk from a mate at work of a house on Little Cornwall, in need of renovation. He was capable with his hands, an avid joiner, and willing to try other D.I.Y. tasks. So talk of this house in Griffin Street was just an appetiser for John.

One bright Sunday afternoon, Kitty took into account John's hopes and wishes, by suggesting they took a stroll to Griffin Street to survey for themselves the area and property that John had in mind. What Kitty had not realised was that the walk was not leisurely at all. Griffin

Street, off the busy Rossendale Road, was a good hour away on foot from their present home in Duke Bar.

The couple found themselves joining a parade of people making their way along Harold Avenue towards the main road. They coasted two or three abreast, some ladies carrying flowers, while children held hands with their parents. Most were dressed in gaily coloured outfits, just a few in befitting dark shades. It dawned on Kitty that these people were heading for Burnley Cemetery, which John had mentioned was situated on the peripheral side of the estate.

As she admired the fusion of the variety of flowers, plants and greenery of the passing gardens, the blue sky up above, she thought how wondrous life had become; her baby stirred as she walked. It was obvious to Kitty that not all the crowd were mourners, many were attending to the graves of their loved ones, not merely out of respect, but for pleasure and celebration of life.

As Kitty approached Little Cornwall, they left the procession, turning right into the cobbled street. Number five was the third house from the bottom. What caught Kitty's attention immediately, was the eight-foot high stone wall, hard, cold, and of a greyish brown colour, which dominated the length of the street. The corporation housing estate which they had just walked through seemed a million miles away.

The 'Ginny Run' was a rail track which started at the Hapton Valley Pit, continuing running parallel with the cemetery, under Rossendale Road and in front of Griffin Street, till it met its end at the top of Tilly's field. Here, slack left over from the mined coal was dumped. Even though it did not burn very well, it came to the rescue of many poor families who used it to mingle with both coal and coke.

John expected her to be as thrilled with all this as he was, but being a man, he did not see the lack of frills that this house had to offer. To Kitty, it looked neglected and needed much tender loving care in order to restore it to any sort of home. She did not want to dampen John's enthusiasm, so she smiled and nodded in agreement to all he said that he would do to make 5, Griffin Street a palace for Kitty and their baby.

John and Kitty made their way home to Duke Bar, which seemed much further, maybe because Kitty's spirits were low. She felt as though the tide had receded and wasn't going to come rushing back. John's world was spinning on its axle and would not slow down. Their solicitor completed financial and conveyancing legalities, and the young couple moved into their new home regardless of its state of decay. Kitty felt nerve-rackingly edgy at the thought of facing new neighbours in a new part of town. She worried how they would judge her moving into such an impoverished house. Would they condemn them because they disapproved of the Irish, as some folks in the cities had? But her worries were unfounded.

They had barely walked into the kitchen when Kitty heard a tap on the front door. A tall lady with short wavy, sandy-coloured hair and hazel eyes, introduced herself as Rose, who lived next door at number seven. Rose suited her name. She had a strong Lancashire accent, yet her voice was soft and quiet. There was something else about Rose; she oozed genuineness. As Kitty wrestled with thoughts of narrow-mindedness regarding her roots, the barriers came down, tumbling like the walls of Jericho. In an instant the two young women were building a strong foundation for companionship.

The most urgent of jobs in the house was the electricity. Electricians were expensive to hire, but in most cases essential. But John being John, found himself in Woolworth's department store one day, shopping for lightbulbs, when he discovered a real treasure. This was a pocket-sized booklet entitled, *'All you need to know about Electricity'*. John picked up the book with a degree of curiosity and interest, then bought it for sixpence. Those six pennies saved John two week's wages.

That weekend he abandoned all other jobs, sat in his favourite armchair, which his Auntie Maggie and Uncle Pat had kindly donated, as he read and reread the instructions on *'How to rewire your own house'*.

Kitty began to feel justly proud of all John's hard work, for he worked tirelessly in the foundry, then during the evening, and most of the weekend, he concentrated on their house.

Meanwhile Kitty's belly was swelling; her baby was due to be born towards the end of the summer. She had lovingly feathered her nest with lovely crocheted blankets in pastel shades, and snowy white nappies were piled alongside finely knitted matinée coats.

Nervous anxiety began to build up in Kitty when she talked through the birthing process, but Rose, already a mother herself, reassured her that she would drop in most mornings for a brew and a chat. Rose's visits here were twofold; she enjoyed her new-found friend's company, savouring nuggets of gossip, but she also wanted to look out for Kitty, in order to look after her. One morning

Kitty mentioned to Rose her fears of what might happen when she went into labour.

"Eh don't worry Kitty, a young lass like you, it'll be like shelling peas," affirmed Rose.

Kitty laughed, and tried to dismiss the butterflies fluttering around in her stomach.

September dawned, and routinely John rose for his work in the foundry, unaware that Kitty had lain awake waiting for daybreak as a nagging back pain had persisted since the early hours. It was now seven o'clock, and both Kitty and John were unsure whether it was time to move to the maternity hospital.

"I'll make a cup of tea, then go for Rose," John suggested at 7:45 a.m. for he knew that Rose would be up preparing Valerie for school.

The urgent sound of knocking gave Rose a start. At a glance she saw John's eyes appealing for help. Taking Valerie's hand she quickly moved to number five.

"Oh Kitty dear, how long have you been like this?" Rose asked on seeing Kitty with one hand on her belly whilst leaning on the back of the sofa.

"It's gone on most of the night Rose," moaned Kitty.

Rose offered to telephone for the ambulance and told Kitty to stay calm.

Kitty's labour was slow and laboriously long. As they were escorted into the delivery room, her nostrils flared at the smell of disinfectant. On the bed, in the room which was cold and foreboding, Kitty scrunched and gripped the white cotton sheet covering her, but there was little relief. She flung her hands to the back of the bed as yet another wave of exhausting pain coursed through her.

At this moment a stern-looking nurse in a starched white apron appeared at the door. In a steely voice she demanded Kitty remove her hands and stop trying to climb the wall!

Kitty searched the whitewashed surroundings for shadows; she needed her mammy. Her mammy did not appear! As she drifted in and out of consciousness her mind focused on her friend Rose.

Realising Rose and many other women had been through all this before her, Kitty remembered the wise words of her friend, "It is a pain you soon forget." At this stage she relaxed a little.

The nurse in the starched apron became gentler as she spoke. "Do you mind if I examine you Kitty dear?" She raised the sheet whilst speaking. The baby's dark crown was showing. "With the next pain lovey push," she instructed.

Kitty pushed and toiled.

The nurse now shouted, "Pant Kitty pant! Right just one more push, come on now, one more."

Pushing with all her might Kitty felt a warm sliver and no more pain.

"Oh! Kitty, you have produced a bonny baby girl, with a mass of jet-black hair. Have you chosen a name for your baby?"

"Yes," Kitty replied with relief, "we're going to call her Joan." Within minutes mother and child were bonding, as Joan suckled on her mother.

John was allowed in the room to meet the new arrival. His heart raced with pride and pleasure as he cradled their first-born. He carefully checked his eight and a half pound daughter. Her fluffy-black hair looked similar to a Grenadier guard's busby. She had chubby cheeks, and a chin with a tiny dimple in the middle. Her pink cherub lips completed the picture.

John whispered to Kitty, "When the jobs are finished we will save up to take Joan to meet her ancestral family in Ireland."

Reflections of the Emerald Isle, warm green fields, and sleepy valleys flashed before Kitty. In her soft Gaelic tones the words rolled from her tongue, "Oh John Manning, what a gem of a man you are."

Five days later Kitty arrived home to Little Cornwall with her darling daughter, and life was suddenly busy. The days had slyly become cooler and shorter, autumn was creeping up unexpectedly, but Kitty was aglow with warmth and love for her family.

Chapter Six

The winter was harsh but happy, and as February gave way to March the annual package of Shamrock arrived from Dublin. John had a collection of letters from his family across the Irish Sea. These contained the news of who was working where, and which brother was courting which colleen? His mum periodically sent him the local newspaper, thus enabling him to keep in touch with the local community he grew up in. It gave him a satisfying feeling, like that of a branch still attached to the vine, being sprinkled with water and fed at regular intervals. He wore his Shamrock with patriotic pride, and some was always pinned to his black felt beret every March 17th.

That first St. Patrick's day spent at 5, Griffin Street John decided to paint the outside window frames and doors a lovely emerald green in declaration of his love for Ireland. It was at this time that Kitty announced that she was pregnant for the second time; the news absolutely delighted John. Joan had brought an ocean of pleasure to their house which was now transformed into a home.

Rose and Kitty were companions in arms, sharing the highs and lows of everyday life. Little Cornwall was a fellowship, where they all helped one another out by passing on clothes, and even furniture.

Rose would often say to Kitty, "I've got some good hot water left in the boiler, can I do any washing for you?"

This was how life was, with everyone working for the common good.

Kitty thought wistfully, "Isn't life grand!"

The autumn of 1948 saw the arrival of John Manning Junior. He had fought his way into the world only twelve months following Joan's birth, causing Kitty considerable agony as he weighed in at eleven pounds and one ounce. She swore to John that they did not need any more children now that they had one of each sex, and vowed to discuss family planning with Betty, the local midwife, with or without John's approval. Although unplanned, his appearance into the world brought immense joy to Kitty and John. Joan had been a pleasant baby, but one worry which Kitty had, was that her childhood may be cut short owing to the demands of another baby.

Joan became the little mother to John, as Kitty nursed him, Joan would imitate her mother and try to feed her dolly. In one way this brought their mother and daughter relationship closer. Even at such an early age, they did things together, and Kitty encouraged Joan to play with John. The two babies would often be seen in the same pram, one at the top and the other at the bottom.

At times Joan would revert back a stage, and demand to be carried on account that she could not walk as she was "Ony baby Mammy," as she often reminded her parents in her own dulcet tones.

Happiness bounced in Kitty's chest as she made her way to the Odeon Cinema through the crowds, which had already formed into a long queue resembling a crocodile, all huddled together to keep out the cold. Tonight was the first showing of the much awaited film, *'Gone with the Wind'*, starring the gorgeous Clarke Gable. Tonight Kitty would enjoy her job even more than usual, as she too wanted to see this film. One of the perks of her job was being able to see all the films.

Kitty loved romantic stories; she did not care much for the Westerns, but she tried to remember them, so that she could tell John all about them. At first she would sit open-mouthed, totally absorbed in the screen, often unaware that the latecomers needed to be shown to their seats, as it was pitch-dark once the film was in progress.

Kitty had been working part-time, during the evenings at the recently opened picture house as an usherette. There was a thrill which excited Kitty when she put on her uniform. It was of a deep crimson trimmed with gold, and had gold shiny buttons. She wore a little hat like the American soldiers wore, and carried a torch to show the customers to their seats.

During the interval Kitty walked down to the front of the cinema carrying a tray full of goodies, these included little tubs of ice-cream, ice-lollies and boxes of smarties, fruit gums and chocolate creams. The only people who bought the smarties were the Teddy boys who wanted to impress the girl they were with, but Kitty thought it would take more than a box of smarties to do the trick they were hoping for at the end of the night!

Life for the Mannings became very settled, money was more available now Kitty was earning, and John spent most of his spare time improving their home. Joinery was John's forté, so bit by bit, and season by season, he started making new window frames. If Kitty was not working on a Saturday night, then she and John would go to the local pub, which was appropriately named *'The Griffin Hotel'*. It was only a stone's throw away, which made it easier for them to acquire a babysitter.

By now Joan was already settled in school, and John had just started. He readily adjusted to school life because Joan looked out for him; so he was a confident little boy, always willing to please everyone. They both attended St. Augustine's Roman Catholic School in Rosegrove. It may have looked dismal from the outside, but appearances were deceiving here. The children were loved and nurtured, and Miss Hornby, the head teacher, could often be seen in the playground with children gathered around her skirts.

However Kitty was restless, she felt a sense of loss with her children becoming more independent, and told John how she felt. The problem was soon solved, Kitty would have another baby. That decided, John and Kitty prepared for the arrival of their third child.

Kathleen was born at home with help from Betty, the local midwife. The baby arrived in November 1952, and was a mixture of both John and Kitty, whereas Joan resembled Kitty whilst John resembled his father. Rose was doing the neighbourly thing by looking after the children. Joan thought baby Kathleen was beautiful.

John grudgingly agreed but said in an impish voice, "When will you be sending her back?"

This turned their smiles into laughter.

Betty with her sleeves still rolled said, "Out of the mouths of babes!"

The months gradually turned into years as Kathleen grew up with the neighbourhood children. She attended the same school as Joan and John. Kathleen only put up with lessons; it did not interest her to be a great scholar. She liked dancing, playing with skipping ropes and doing craft lessons best of all. Kathleen liked to dress up in Joan and Kitty's shoes and clothes.

Her friend was Eileen Smith, who lived at the back of Kathleen on Hapton Street; they went to school together. In fact all the children from Little Cornwall who attended St. Augustine's, or Rosegrove, which was the Protestant school nearby, were taken to school by the older children and brought back safely to their parents.

Chapter Seven

'Puffing Billy' came hooting and spluttering its way into Rosegrove railway station sounding as angry as ever. Kathleen hid behind her dad's long belted overcoat clinging to him. The steam train was given this nickname because she thought it reminded her of a big, long, wingless dragon made of steel. She was terrified of all the smoke it bellowed out. The train seemed to be alive, and it was so grotesque and ugly. The frontal view appeared to have eyes that glared, inflamed by the heat from the engine.

For the last decade John had rewarded himself for his hard work by continually taking Kitty and their children twice a year to visit relatives in Ireland, just as he vowed to Kitty on the day that Joan was born. He worked 'foreigners', additional work at the weekends, doing jobs for other people. John could be seen with his long ladders strapped to his old push-bike, his overalls splattered with snowcem. He would paint anyone's house in whatever colour they requested, except green.

Green was strictly reserved for 5, Griffin Street! He did not mind all the extra hard work and long hours; as the whole family reaped the benefit. The profit he received helped to pay for their vacation to their homeland.

Two train journeys were necessary from Burnley to arrive at the port of Holyhead. But once settled on the mainline train from Manchester the ride was quite comfortable, as they usually managed to acquire a carriage to themselves. The children would spread themselves across their parents' laps, snuggling down to rhythmic sleep as the train clattered along into the darkness of nightfall.

The travellers would be woken by the sound of a loud whistle and a guard shouting, "Holyhead! Anyone for the port of Holyhead?"

The huge sailing vessel was docked awaiting the holiday-makers, immigrants returning home and a small number of business people struggling to embark by the narrow, wobbly, up-hill bridge, that reached out from shore to ship. Mr. Manning dragged the two portmanteaus, whilst Mrs. Manning was aided by her two older children and the sailors on board. Joan had now turned thirteen-years of age and was almost as tall as her mother, and John Junior was twelve-years old, so both were fully-laden with the necessary hand luggage.

The familiar smells of fish mingled with oil and diesel fuel. The taste of salt in the air, and the mist that drifted in from the sea were pleasant reminders of how time had elapsed over the years. Once the ferry drifted out into the Irish Sea, John found a sheltered spot on the upper deck, where he could hug his girls under his enormous fawn overcoat, which acted as a parapet against the fresh winds and sea spray, which hopefully would help to control Kathleen's sea-sickness. John Junior kept company with his mother on the lower levels. A cabin had been out of the question, ever since they had taken three children, due to the expense.

As the dock of Dun Laoghaire drew nearer, the family played the ritual game of *'I spy for Uncle Paddy'*. Paddy, John's brother, always met them to take them to Grandma's (Marzie as she was known). Paddy was usually easy to spot, as he was always meticulously dressed in his elegant suit and trilby hat.

Marzie used to say, "Paddy you favour one of those fancy American fellows who come in off the big liners, swaying like a movie star, so you do!"

Paddy caught sight of John and his family, and ran over and grabbed John by the shoulders saying, "You look wonderful, what a great time we will all have." If he noticed how pale and thin Kitty looked, or how dark the deep circles appeared under her once bright shining Irish eyes, he did not say.

He simply welcomed her, "Ah Kitty, nice to see you all."

Grandma's house was owned by the council, and was situated on the fringe of the river-bank. The whole family would spend hours idling time away, sometimes dreaming, as they watched all kinds of sailing boats pass by. There were houseboats boasting a ray of colours, sloops and small passenger vessels. Everyone would wave in synchronisation, the international sign language for unified friendliness.

Grandma shared her home with her two unmarried children, Paddy and Annie. Annie had a great passion for

Yorkshire Terriers. She bred them and treated them like babies. Kathleen would sit by her Gran and beg her to tell her of the 'good old days' when Granddad was still living.

"Ah!," she'd say, "Jayzus, Mary and Joseph, I'm lucky to have a roof over me head, so I am. He died of natural causes you know love, God rest his soul," she blessed herself continually whilst telling the tale. "He'd bank the fire up with as much turf as he could, ease back and fall sound asleep in his comfy armchair, and low and behold Jayzus, Mary and Joseph the chimney would be on fire, so it would."

Kathleen would give a hearty laugh, the image conjured up in her young mind was that of Granddad being burnt alive, like the flames of hell-fire!

Sunday being the Sabbath, everyone went off to church, gathering later at Marzie's house. Lunch was served in relays on account of the number of guests. Aunts, uncles, cousins, grandchildren and great-grandchildren were all there. Once in a while the men would try a Guinness in the local public house whilst the women caught up with idle talk. Nothing went down better at Marzie's than tea and gossip.

Early one evening when Kathleen was playing skipping with Doreen and Kathleen - (there were three children named Kathleen in the extended Manning family) she thought her eyes were deceiving her when Uncle Billy's truck came hurtling round the corner at speed, with John dangling from the back, gripping on with his hands for dear life. He'd had one or two Guinness too many. This was the one and only time that Kathleen ever saw her dad drunk!

All too soon the holiday came to an end as all good things do. Sat in the back of Uncle Paddy's smart car, Kitty became engrossed in the passing landscapes. The roaming hills were dotted with forest glades, in the richest shades of green. Deep valleys and glorious beaches were filled with crystallised waters. If England owned such beauty she had not yet found it.

The trip had been tinged with sadness, for Kitty was harbouring a secret from her family. She had visited the doctor on several occasions, and already had a hospital appointment. She wanted to memorise Erin's beauty, and capture it in her mind for evermore.

Up on the deck of the ferry, watching Ireland slip away into the distance, Kitty and Joan stood together like sisters in intimate conversation. The breeze was fresh as Kitty turned looking seaward.

Her hair was swept from her face by the wind, and salty tears stung her cheeks as she thought out loud, "I'll never come home again!"

Joan turned sharply, unsure she had heard correctly, but the crestfallen look on Kitty's face would not allow Joan to dig deeper. She stared down at the foaming waves of the sea, as they broke into spindrift. Joan's cup was overspilling with anxiety; Kitty's was filled with dread and emotion.

Only John knew that Kitty had cancer, for even Rose did not know at this stage. Cancer was a word which really did not exist, for it was never spoken. Instead euphemisms were used - and even they were only spoken in whispers. Both John and Kitty were put at ease by the medical professionals, and they really did believe them when they said the illness could be treated, so Kitty bravely endured the treatment.

John became the 'housewife', he took the children for their clothes, and all the groceries were purchased from the local shopkeeper, known to all as 'Lizzy Boss'. Joan, who was now fourteen-years old, managed to undertake most of the housework. She realised that Kitty was unwell, but she just thought that she was tired and overworked now that she was getting older. Teenagers always think that their parents are much older than their years, and in this Joan was no exception. Kathleen needed some new clothes Kitty informed John. In truth Kathleen did not *really* need them, but Kitty was trying to maintain some kind of normality to life at 5, Griffin Street.

Kathleen buzzed around hardly able to control her excitement, her dad was taking her into town shopping. She knew she would get to choose her *own* clothes, because lately dad somehow seemed so preoccupied, that Kathleen seemed to get her own way without much of a struggle from her parents. She was not a spoilt child, but just liked her own way with the little things, like going to bed later, and staying longer playing in Eileen's house.

The shopping day arrived, and they walked down into the town. Later they were going to catch the bus home. Kathleen did not think this unfair, because it meant that she could spend a longer time on a one to one basis with her father.

Her brother John had gone fishing with his friend Tom Haggs, whilst Joan stayed with her mum and did some cleaning. It caused Joan some anxiety that Rose was in their house more frequently, always bringing in clean washing and ironing, but it did not occur to Joan that her mother had not been doing these jobs of late.

Kathleen was to have a new coat for best and some new shoes. She had not even outgrown her shoes, but Kitty said that she could not have a new coat and continue to wear the same shabby shoes. After a very perplexing hour for John the coat was chosen. It was bright red and without a collar, but had a scarf of black and white dog-toothed check, which apparently, according to the shop assistant, was all the rage. This sealed the sale for Kathleen, because she had not seen anyone else with a coat without a collar. The shoes were quickly chosen as soon as Kathleen stood in front of the window of Freeman, Hardy and Willis - *'The best shoe shop ever in Burnley'*, according to the slogan on the door. It was a fully contented Kathleen who arrived back in Griffin Street that Saturday afternoon.

John was fairly exhausted; he had plenty of more important issues on his mind that day, the main one was that Kitty did not seem to be getting any better.

Kathleen proudly showed off her new things to Rose, Joan and Kitty, who all agreed that John had done a great job on his shopping expedition. The shoes were the best that Kathleen had imagined, black, shiny patent leather. They were so dainty, that Kathleen thought that her dancing would improve if she wore them to dance in. They had narrow cross-over straps across the instep, but most importantly of all, they had Cuban-heels. Up till now Kathleen had only worn fairly flat childish shoes, or very practical school shoes, but these were special, and they made **her** feel extra special, and lately this was just what she needed.

Father Corker blessed the congregation, and left the altar making his way into the vestry. This was the sign the people were waiting for before they could leave the pews and make their way outside. They all filed out of church; the adults putting something in the collection box on the way out, even though there had already been two collections during Mass. Kathleen, Joan and John had been given a penny each to put into the box during the service, so the children just blessed themselves on their way out with holy water, then made a quick sign of the cross, for they knew then that church was over for the day.

Friends and families gathered outside chatting and catching up with the week's events. The Mannings always went to church at St. Mary Magdalene's, even though they attended St. Augustine's school. Kitty had not been with the family to church for some time now owing to her illness, and her admissions to hospital. Kathleen had her new red coat on, and of course the exceptional new black, patent, Cuban-heeled shoes. They made a tapping sound when Kathleen walked, so she emphasised this, because it drew attention to the shoes, and people looked and admired them.

John knew quite a few people in the congregation, who all made discreet enquires after Kitty's welfare. John always stayed to chat to a tall, lean, mature man who wore a trilby hat, this man was always accompanied by a girl of about the same age as Kathleen. She had lovely red hair fastened in plaits, just like Kathleen's, and always held onto her dad's hand, just as Kathleen did. Today, the girl wore a coat which was identical to Kathleen's, except for the colour; the girl's was dark green, but with the same chequered scarf. The two young girls glanced at each other, looking each other up and down, to find to their absolute amazement that they were both wearing the same special shoes, the black, shiny, patent Cuban-heels. This was Kathleen's first memory of her friend Margaret.

For four days Kitty kept the buff-coloured envelope with the red hospital logo stamped across the front, hidden in the top drawer of her dressing table. For four days John had asked Kitty had there been any post, or any word from Christie's? Four times Kitty had denied John. She had opened the letter on Monday morning, but felt more pain on the realisation, as she read the contents that she had to be admitted at 2:00 p.m. on the 23rd November 1963.

"Kathleen's birthday," she spoke to herself, for there was no one around to hear her. "How could fate deal out such a cruel blow?"

As John arrived home from work on Friday teatime, before he could ask again, Kitty gave him the envelope.

Anguish and disappointment crept across his face. "I'll tell her," he said.

Ten days before Kathleen's eleventh birthday John told his three children that their mother was going to the hospital for radium therapy, on November 23rd.

"But that's our Kathleen's birthday," protested Joan.

"Yes I know," John answered in a low voice, "but it can't be helped. There will be other birthdays Kathleen," he looked across at his youngest daughter, reassuringly.

She hadn't expected a fuss or a party, she knew her mum was too ill for that. Kitty had already lost her shine and zest for life. This illness had sapped all her strength.

The morning of the hospital appointment broke cold and damp as almost any other day in November. Kathleen rose not knowing what to think. Everyone had wished her happy birthday, and given her cards and presents.

Joan and John had pulled her hair, and in unison asked, "What would you like, cock, goose, feather or rose?"

"I'd like to make a wish," demanded Kathleen.

"All right then, let her make a wish," said Joan, "but it must be a secret, keep it to yourself."

"I wish for us all to go to Manchester with Mummy, and that she soon gets better," Kathleen thought as she closed her eyes.

The whole family sat and ate breakfast dispiritedly, almost like 'silent meals', no one knowing what would be the right thing to say. Kathleen could hardly swallow her porridge oats for the heavy lump constricting her throat. The plan was for Joan to go to the hospital with her parents, and John Junior and Kathleen to go to school as normal. Their good friend, Auntie Rose, would take care of them afterwards. Kathleen sat staring, thinking of the day ahead. She would be brought out of the class to stand at the front wearing a paper crown, while all the boys and girls sang 'Happy Birthday'. She hated being made to stand on ceremony, with everyone looking at her, she would much rather blend into the background.

John Junior remained silent. Joan looked at her mum and thought of the number of times she had been disobedient, refusing to wash up or run an errand.

This reflection brought into view the picture of her mum sat in her chair uttering the words, "You'll miss me when I'm gone."

Joan felt remorseful.

John broke the silence having seen the sadness in his children's faces. "How about we all go with mum today?"

"Can we?" Kathleen looked up, her eyes opening wider, "Oh, please can we?" she pleaded.

The atmosphere lightened as they all prepared for the unknown.

Kitty walked through the doors into Christie Hospital where she was to spend the next two months. The attempt to cure her was so destructive that it shrank the flesh to her bones. It tinged her pallor a bisque colour. Kitty's only ability on her return to 5, Griffin Street was to walk aided by the hallway wall, slowly and painfully to the front room, which had now become her make-shift bedroom.

Kathleen was both shocked and frightened by her mum's decline. She hardly recognised her.

John would say, "Kathleen just take this cup of tea through to your mum love."

Kathleen did so willingly, but as she reached the bedroom door she would hover nervously, thinking, "Shall I, shan't I?" wary of meeting the gaze of her mum's glassy eyes.

Kitty had one last duty to attend to, it gnawed at her like a rat did with a rope. "We have to get Kathleen's school uniform sorted out John," she moaned between pain and restless sleep.

"Don't worry Kitty love," John soothed, as he stroked her hair away from her brow, "we've got her a gymslip, two white blouses, a tie, cardigan, and everything. She'll try them all on for you later."

Kathleen should have been looking forward to starting her new school, St. Hilda's Roman Catholic Secondary Modern, but her mind was in a whirl. She modelled the uniform, twirling for her mum.

This brought a smile to Kitty's wan face, and she just whispered, "Beautiful!"

How proud she felt one can only guess.

Kitty passed away silently and peacefully on the 22nd July 1964, leaving a trail of destruction in her wake. The calendar with moveable figures, which sat on the television, was never altered for the next fifteen years. John was left heartbroken, and his world felt empty. He could not move on. How could God steal his Kitty? How could John ever forgive Him? Whereas once John had heard a symphony play, now only a big drum pounded in his head.

The children in some respects felt they had lost both parents. John only saw the surface of his children's grief, for he was completely saturated with his own sorrow. Kathleen studied her rainbow from her place of solace, the front bedroom window. Seeing families enjoy the gymkhana at Griffin Farm in the short distance, brought loathing and envy to her heart. She could feel the irony of the cheering and laughing on this bright sunny day. What had life in store for her now? Would she ever find her pot of gold?

It was a very brave Kathleen who walked through the black iron gates, and down the sloping driveway to the entrance of St. Hilda's that warm Monday morning in August. Of course she had Joan, her big sister, to guard and protect her from the customary taunts to the first year girls, which were all done in fun mind you. However, it was a not so brave Kathleen who had to follow the line of girls out of the hall into a make-do classroom. It was make-do because it served as the dining room also.

In total there were three classrooms which everyday had to be transformed to make way for hungry girls to eat their lunch. Kathleen listened for her name to be called, telling her where she was to sit in the class. The teachers had been informed that Mrs. Manning, Joan's mother, had died during the summer break; they had also been made aware that the youngest family member would be a first-year girl, and she should be treated with kid gloves for a while.

"Kathleen Manning?" enquired Miss Selkirk, a young recently qualified teacher.

As acknowledgement, Kathleen held up her hand.

"Can you please sit there," she pointed. "Yes the second desk."

Kathleen sat down and looked at the girl next to her. It was the girl from church, the girl with Kathleen's special shoes, the Cuban-heels. They smiled at each other. It was later on in the day when the girl behind Kathleen purposely squirted ink from her fountain pen onto Kathleen's back.

The girl sat next to Kathleen said, "You've got some ink on your collar, your mum will have to wash it, I think it'll come out."

Kathleen just looked at her and felt safe, she said, "I haven't got a mum, she's just died."

"I'm Margaret," the girl said, "shall we be friends?"

That night Margaret told her mum about her new friend, who did not have a mum of her own anymore.

Mrs. Hand said, "I'll be her mum, bring her here and let me meet her," but she mumbled to herself lightly, "I haven't got three daughters, I now have four!"

Kathleen and Margaret became firm friends from that very first day at St. Hilda's school; Kathleen was invited to 1, Paisley Street, and Margaret was invited to 5, Griffin Street in return. Whilst none of the girls ever called Mrs. Hand 'mum' she often took on the role of a mother to all the girls. For Kathleen, Mrs. Hand did the motherly duties of taking both girls to the dentist, to the doctors and suchlike.

There was one instance when both Margaret and Kathleen had to go to the dentist to have teeth removed with the aid of the dreaded gas. Getting both girls home to Paisley Street was an ordeal for Mrs. Hand, as both girls were unsteady and drowsy. They resembled the drunks coming home from the pubs on Accy Road. She would manage to steady one of the girls, then the other would sway or spit out a mouthful of blood. Once home both girls were put to bed until they had come round from the anaesthetic, and Kathleen waited there until her dad came to collect her when he had finished work.

Chapter Eight

Life for the circle of friends was enriched at their senior school. They all met new companions, yet remained as close as ever, as close as loving sisters. With the onset of adolescence, names were shortened, as life buzzed with a need to catch and savour every new experience. Due to her academic ability, Christine was in a different form at school to Margaret and Kath. Being a year older, Carole had already faced the daunting move alone, but she did find new acquaintances. They all missed the girls who had been privileged enough to move on to grammar school, and the boys who now attended St. Theodore's.

On Friday, Saturday and Sunday evenings they found themselves congregating in the old St. Mary Magdalene's school yard. They seemed drawn there like magnets, for they enjoyed one another's company, exchanging new discoveries in the ever changing world of the 1960's.

Skipping and games were no longer prevalent, but homework and new school subjects like Science, Scripture, Latin and French were now topics of conversation. Latest fashion, haircuts and music, were naturally also on the agenda. There was a shyness now between the boys and girls, but also a caring innocence.

Around this time a new curate arrived in the parish to help Father Corker prepare for his retirement. His name was Father Fraher. The new priest quietly observed this troop of young teenagers, who sheltered from the rain wearing flimsy nylon macs, which appeared to be the up to the minute trend. This impractical clothing did nothing to keep the rain out, or the warmth in. The girls huddled together under a couple of umbrellas, which threatened to blow inside out. The lads tried to appear tough, by weathering the elements, each secretly hoping that someone else would suggest an early trip home.

After two or three weekends, and a lot of thought, the young priest decided he liked the look of the youngsters who assembled in the yard. They weren't annoying or badly behaved, just in need of shelter and a few activities to occupy their time. His moral sense told him the old school hall that housed so many assemblies, need not lay redundant at the weekends, but could establish itself as a youth club. After much deliberation he introduced himself to them one Friday evening, and asked out of genuine curiosity why they met on these premises?

"We've nowhere to go," declared Margaret.

Instantly the priest's thoughts drifted back to his own early life growing up in Ireland, recalling the number of young people who hung around the street corners aimlessly. "Would it help if I opened the school hall? We could maybe open a youth club," he offered.

They could not believe their luck! There was such a place at the bottom of Sandy Gate, but it attracted mainly

Teddy boys, besides which you had to be at least fifteen-years of age to gain admittance, whereas some of these children were barely thirteen.

"Of course, you understand before you get too excited there will have to be ground rules. For instance there must be no fighting, smoking, swearing or alcohol, and definitely no hanky-panky," Father Fraher said with an expression of concern in his voice.

"That's all right Father, we won't be doing anything like that," chirped up Michael Flint, with a gleam in his eye.

The boys may have had hanky-panky in mind, but all they wanted was a place that was their own, something just for them, a youth club - *their* youth club!

"Well, I've discussed the matter with some of the senior parishioners, and most of them are in agreement. However if the rules are broken they'll be down on us immediately."

The teenagers felt the priest was a friend – one of the crowd. In fact Father Fraher turned out to be a much needed breath of fresh air.

"What do you think you'll need to run a place where you can all gather and keep out of trouble?" he asked them. Then he listened tentatively as they all put in suggestions of a record player, a table-tennis table and perhaps a badminton court, and definitely a tuck shop.

"I'll speak to the boss and see if we can oblige. It doesn't sound like too much to ask really." He spoke with optimism raising the lads' and lasses' spirits.

They felt elated, started planning what to wear, which records would be the best to dance to, and what goodies they could sell in the tuck shop?

Father Fraher had rallied Paul, Wilf and Tony to help set things up. Even one or two engaged couples, who were saving to get married, volunteered their time, for adult supervision was paramount for the smooth running of things. An agreement was made to open the club two evenings a week. The nights were agreed upon as Friday and Sunday.

On the opening night the children re-entered their old school hall with a degree of excitement. No longer was there any trace of fear as they peeped through the bright green heavy doors. The stone stairway seemed much narrower with the passing of time. Striding the steps two at a time, carrying their limited record collection, they stepped into the hall, then made their way to the corner where the D.J. had set out his stall.

"We'd best make sure we don't break any ground rules." Margaret whispered.

"The crucifix is up there," laughed Pat, a new friend from Stoops Estate.

Christine came between them, "Big brother's watching you!"

"Oh shut up Christine," called out Margaret, "we'll be frightened of moving in a minute."

The three of them began shuffling their feet attempting to dance to the *Small Faces* singing *Sha la la la lee*, whilst Steven Bradbury and Steven Morrison played table tennis in time to the rhythm. A group of giggling girls had gathered at the side of the table cheering for whoever they fancied, as they scored a point.

All week the girls had discussed what to wear, and still could not decide until the very last minute on Friday night. Fashion was worn with attitude. It was 'in' to be seen in a slip of a mini skirt, teamed with a knitted skinny rib, polo-neck sweater. Some females wore culottes. This item of clothing was like a dress, but the skirt part ventured into shorts. They all thought them trendy. If they didn't already own a pair, then that would be what they would be saving for next. Their shoes were flat, and the latest accessory was a pair of tan-coloured tights. Tights were wonderful according to the older girls who had had to mess with stockings and suspenders up till then. Though if you had asked the older boys which *they* thought were the best, it would always be the latter.

The girls had now got into the habit of borrowing each other's clothes, giving the appearance to the boys that each girl had several outfits. This prompted the Trickett sisters and Pat to find some source of income to pay for all the girlie things teenagers wanted, like nail polish, lip gloss, and of course records. The three of them had to take jobs delivering the newspapers in the mornings, and often after school, or on a Friday tea-time collecting the money. Margaret and Kath did not need to undertake a part-time job, as everything that they needed was provided for at home.

Father Fraher entered the building with trepidation, wondering if he had been right to open a youth club, or was he asking for trouble, as a minority of older members of the parish had implied. He was pleased, and even impressed by what he saw, and although there were only a dozen people there initially, he promised they'd soon have a full register, as he would announce the club's opening times at Mass in future.

Kath spent most evenings sat with her dad, they relied on each other completely. John was like a record stuck in a groove, for grieving had left him trapped. Moving on after losing his precious Kitty had proved impossible, but he and his daughter now found a mutual solace.

Carole hadn't the same free spirit as her younger sister, and being a plodder, homework took her hours. Audrey's mental instability held the family firmly in its grip. Being the eldest, Carole felt obliged to shoulder some of the responsibilities for her siblings, so she hadn't yet ventured back to her old school.

The sisters shared the front bedroom of their parents' semi. Once tucked up and lights out, conversation usually followed.

"You'll never guess where I've been tonight," bragged Christine.

"No I can't guess where you have been tonight," repeated Carole wearily.

"Well Father Fraher has opened St. Mary Mag's School Hall up as a youth club on Friday and Sunday nights; you can come if you want, it's great, there's plenty to do. Everyone takes their records and table tennis bats, it's fabulous, you'll have to find something to wear though, they all wear really smart clothes, you know like the 'mods' do." Christine did not come up for air, did not stop to breathe in, and her excitement threatened to keep her awake.

Carole did think about it, wondering what on earth would she want to go back to 'that place' for? But nevertheless when Sunday came she decided to investigate for herself. For Carole, revisiting the place of her misery, was something that she was dreading. Her friends told her not to think of it as school, because they were going there to enjoy themselves. She entered the building, wearing grey hipster checked flares and a skinny ribbed jumper, she realised at once that they were right, and all thoughts of oppression were quickly banished, and most importantly there were no teachers present to spoil things.

The number of young people attending soon multiplied fast as news spread by word of mouth, and it became a prestigious place to be seen in. Barriers between different denominations, quickly broke down, as it was deemed not necessary to be a Catholic to attend. This was a positive move by the church, and very beneficial to the young people of Burnley, as they developed and adapted healthy attitudes towards others.

St. Mary Magdalene's was a place where many girls tasted their first kiss. Some couples courted there then later married. Father Fraher performed the Sacrament of Matrimony for at least three couples who met at the youth club. He became kinship to the members, 'Evergreen', for all of them knew he'd always be there for them in times of good or bad.

Life began to revolve around Friday and Sunday evenings, growing up in innocence where boys and girls shared the trials of reaching maturity. Friends supported Susan, Paul and Anthony when their father died suddenly at a very young age. For some, this was their first experience of death and sadness. Without realising it the pals became counsellors, just by being there.

Anthony was the one who always embraced the funny side of life. On one occasion when members were expected to refrain from laughter and listen seriously, he had everyone in hysterics including Father Fraher. The priest and senior members of the club felt it wise to offer sex education to the teenagers. Most parents hadn't bothered to broach the subject for fear of embarrassment. The church had now come their aid. Consent had to be sought from legal guardians of anyone under sixteen years of age to watch the fifteen minute animated version of the male and female reproductive system, and the end of the film always led to question time.

"Right," said the speaker. "Thank you boys and girls for listening so patiently." Wringing his hands, he asked if everyone had understood everything, and if not had they any questions?

Anthony being quick to respond stuck up his hand and waited for a prompt. "Sir, if the egg goes around in a cycle, like, how many miles per hour does it travel?" His cheeks glowed bright red as he spluttered and chuckled leaving the volunteer dumbstruck.

Father Fraher bowed his head in amused embarrassment. The school hall echoed with gales of laughter as Anthony felt he'd performed his debut on stage with his aplomb wit.

In the summer of 1966 a 'Fun-Day' had been organised, which was to be held on the Prairie Playing Fields. Youth groups, Girl Guides and Boy Scout troops, Cubs and Brownies all took part in the fund-raising event, which was designed to emulate pure family entertainment. Weeks went into the planning.

St. Mary Magdalene's decided to feature a sporting fixture with partakers dressed as hockey players, footballers and cricketers. Margaret masqueraded as a tennis star in an all white kit. Audrey had knitted a claret and blue polo neck sweater for Carole to wear as a Burnley Football Club Supporter. Another group dressed as St. Trinian's Schoolgirls, in exaggerated school uniforms, giving everyone the chance to add to the fun, relax, and let their hair down.

The weather for June was atrocious. Rain had started early in the morning, leaving the field like a soggy wet sponge. Undaunted, their eagerness not dampened, the youth of St. Mary Magdalene's contributed to the day with enthusiasm, joining in the tug-of-war games, races and other competitive events to entertain the public, whilst raising money for underprivileged children.

Times like these, typically shaped the youngsters into responsible adults, reaping the reward of good grounding. There was the odd occasion when the youngsters overstepped the very fine line of good behaviour. One of those times was when Sheila, an ex-St. Mary Mag's schoolgirl, now at St. Hilda's, was asked to babysit for a trusting neighbour. The occasion became a party when the girls asked the boys round. Sheila was babysitting at Marcia's house, so the guests had to wait until she and her husband had gone out. They would have hidden under the privet hedge of the neighbouring house, but Sheila and her parents lived next door, and so the gang had to keep out of sight until one of the girls came to find them.

Records were blaring, a couple of bottles of cider were being passed around, when suddenly Sheila's mum came through the living-room door at quite a pace. She turned off the record player, scratching a deep groove across the vinyl in her action, and ordered the gang to leave.

She shouted to Sheila with gravity in her voice, "I'll deal with you later lady."

As everyone filed out she spotted Geraldine Holdsworth, and addressed her. "And you Madam, Miss Grammar School girl, I bet this was one of your fancy ideas?"

It was a very embarrassed Sheila who met her friends the following week, not only had she had to succumb to her mother's sarcasm, but she had lost her babysitting job, for which she was paid five shillings. Later her mother felt some remorse, and said that if she promised not to have her mates in the house, she would ask Marcia to reconsider letting her have her job back, now that she had learnt her lesson!

The hardest lesson to learn though, was when one member of the club invited some girls from the Rosegrove area over to visit. These girls were streetwise, and thought it clever to pick a fight with Eileen Pilling. Eileen wasn't scared, as Lynne pulled her hair and fought with her nails like a cat with its claws. What they didn't realise though, was that the spectacle was on show to the priests in the presbytery. The shame and vulgarity of the episode brought Father Fraher marching out.

After splitting the girls apart, he silently emptied the school and locked the door. All the begging and pleading from innocent members was in vain. He felt his position as a newly-appointed Parish Priest left him no option but to close the club down once and for all. So it was that the assembly hall of St. Mary Magdalene's School lay fallow at the weekends yet again.

Some members applied for recruitment at Central Youth Club on Padiham Road, opposite Roebuck Street.

Steve and Trevor, who managed the club, had been granted the whole of the first floor above the Co-op grocery store. There was enough room for a badminton court, table tennis tables and a dance area, where local bands would play at weekends. The impact wasn't quite the same somehow, but still there were some memorable times.

Once the two organisers arranged for the lads and lasses to follow the local custom and climb Pendle Hill at midnight on Halloween. This was a tradition that had been handed down from generation to generation. Naturally everyone wishing to take part had to seek permission from parents or guardians. The Trickett girls were buzzing at the thoughts of the thrill of such an expedition.

Margaret fancied the idea, but wasn't quite sure what she'd wear. "You can't climb a mountain in a skirt, and I don't even possess a pair of pants, never mind jeans," she complained.

"Well, I'm not going," Kath said adamantly. "I can think of better things to do than stay out all night in freezing weather."

"Oh good," Christine thought quickly. "Can I borrow your school shoes? Mine leak, me feet will finish up soaked if I go in them."

"Hang on a minute, who said we could go? We've to ask me dad yet," stated Carole, almost putting a dampener on things.

"We'll talk him round, if Margaret gets to go then he'll let us," Christine replied.

"Yeh, you're right. You ask *your* mum first Margaret, then we'll ask."

It was fine by Mrs. Hand. "If Carole and Christine are going then you can go," she said.

Philip allowed his two daughters on the trip as long as they ate a bowl of his porridge first.

Kath called with her school shoes for Christine at teatime. "Don't let me dad know you've got 'em, he'll go mad if he knows I've let you go climbing in 'em. I've only had 'em three weeks."

"Don't worry," said Christine, "I'll have them back before Monday, all polished and looking like new!"

Pat turned up for her friends at Harold Avenue around 10:00 p.m. where she had to eat the bowl of disgusting cereal.

"Right lasses come and get this down ya." Philip shouted as he dished out the oatmeal.

"Ya can stand the spoon up in this, it'll soon put hairs on ya chest; keeps the cold out ya knows."

"Oh dad I can't eat this, it'll make me sick," cried Carole.

"I can't either Mr. Trickett," said Pat.

"Course ya can, ya not climbing no flaming Pendle Hill till ya do, so come on get it down ya."

Philip left the girls in the kitchen feeling sickly as they tried to eat. But then they had a cunning plan as he lay full length on the settee in the living-room dozing. One by one they tiptoed down the passageway, out the back door then emptied the bowls of porridge down the drain, whilst running the kitchen tap, thus hiding all evidence of their deceit. They woke their dad up with three clean dishes and gained his permission to make their way to Paisley Street for Margaret. They ran along Harold Avenue and across the rec. to Margaret's, for fear that they had possibly blocked the drains with the porridge. Fear didn't stop them laughing though!

Now at Mrs. Hand's they were offered hot chocolate to warm their bellies. This brought smiles to faces, as did Margaret's navy blue tailored linen trouser suit!

Nine youngsters whose average age was fourteen, met Trevor and Steve at 11:00 p.m. for their midnight hike. Armed with flasks of piping hot Oxo, and flashlights, they route marched down beyond the gas works, through Barden towards Pendle Bottoms. Ripples of excitement turned to anxiety as the boys became incensed with telling ghost stories. They told tales of Alice Nutter, the sorceress burnt for her beliefs, and witches flying across blackened skies on their broomsticks.

Trevor led the climb, finding safe footings with the aid of his torch, whilst everyone else followed. All was going well until the rain began lashing their faces. The higher they climbed the boggier the ground became, making squelching sounds as it sucked each footstep in.

In the dark cold night Pendle Hill no longer appeared rich and beautiful, but seemed barren and murky, almost devil-like. Most teenagers were well wrapped up in knitted sweaters, thick woolly socks and anoraks with decent walking shoes, but one girl wore a cream, Jackie Kennedy-style leather coat, as if she was in a fashion show. She became one to focus on, because at least she could be seen in the dark.

Even in such hostile conditions, all reached the summit unaided except for Margaret. Not being the outdoor type, or even remotely sporty, she struggled greatly. As people passed her she clung to sods and rocks as stones were loosened by their tread.

"Help!" she shouted. "Somebody help, there's boulders coming down. Help I'm gonna be killed."

Steve was just a few yards behind her, as he realised this was Margaret as he'd never seen her before, a drama queen doing her performing arts bit. He and Michael Flint took both arms and dragged her to the top. She looked as though she'd been travelling through the high seas.

From such a great height the sleepy valley of Burnley twinkled with thousands of lamplights on full spectacular imagery. Sadly there wasn't time to linger. The plan was to ramble across the top of Pendle Hill ('Old Nick') and down into the village of Sabden.

Without even a glimpse of common courtesy the weather quickly changed, and dawn appeared deceptively. The wind wasn't as strong now, but it still blew cuttingly through their wet clothes, chilling the bones of the wearer savagely. The rain had ceased, leaving behind it a hard cruel frost. It wasn't until now that Christine realised she had lost one of Kath's school shoes in some forsaken bog. Her body was hypothermic, which dulled her mind to the consequences of this.

Reaching Sabden was a long strenuous trek, but the girl in the cream leather coat remembered this was *Whistle down the Wind'* country and danced across the moors like a free spirit, just as the children in the film had, not many years previously.

A country café opened its doors to the Halloween revellers, welcoming them with hot mugs of tea. Each one talked of hot steaming baths and warm beds, whilst waiting for the corporation bus to take them back to

Padiham Road. All decided that the bewitching Pendle Hill was far more appreciated from a distance.

Culturally, the welfare of the children held no limits for the parents. There was a distance between each family, but the common denominator was their offspring. Margaret and friends had been members of Central Youth Club around three months when an unsavoury gang appeared. This gang didn't stay long, only perhaps an hour or so, but on their departure it was discovered that a purse had been stolen from a coat pocket in the cloakroom. No one owned up to the offence, so Steve and Trevor demanded that nobody could leave until the police had arrived and dealt with the matter. The law didn't hurry, and the deadline for Carole and Christine being home had long since expired.

"We're in real trouble now," said Carole, "it's quarter past eleven and work in the morning."

Margaret told her not to worry, as her mum would walk them both home and explain to their dad why they were so late. It was almost midnight when they arrived at Paisley Street.

"Where have you been love?" asked Mrs. Hand, "I've been really worried."

Margaret explained about the missing purse and the police. Her mum was just relieved to see her daughter home safe and well.

"These two will get murdered when they get home, their dad will be pacing the floor."

"It's true Mrs. Hand, he'll go mad," said Christine.

"Right, you get ready for bed Margaret, kettle's just boiled love if you want some cocoa. Ya dad's sat watching telly. I'll get me coat on and walk these lasses home."

Both Carole and Christine gratefully linked arms with their friend's mother, and with high hopes that she could defuse Philip's temper.

As they walked through the door he rose from the settee shouting, "Where the bloody…"

They interrupted him together, "Dad, Mrs. Hand's come to tell you why we're so late."

"Eh, don't shout at 'em Philip lad, someone stole a purse, and they wouldn't let anyone go home until it was found. They knew you'd be worried," explained Margaret's mum.

"Aye, I have and all, but thanks for getting them home, it's bloody murder isn't it? They have ya worried sick, anyway you two, up the dancers, you'll never get up in the morning. Thanks again Mrs. Hand," said Philip. "Will you be all right going over the rec? Leonard will be wondering where **you** are," he spoke a little more light-heartedly.

Only a week later an incident called for Philip's assistance. Kath had spent the evening with Margaret watching television. Mrs. Hand walked her to the rec. and watched as she reached Cog Lane. As Kath made her way along Harold Avenue towards Griffin Street, she was aware of someone not far behind her. His shadow was intercepting hers at a quickening pace. Crossing the road she heard his heavy footsteps coming closer. Glancing over her shoulder she was alarmed to see his long mac swaying. Her only thought was to get help. The Trickett's house was just a few yards away. Kath didn't need to knock as Philip had just coincidentally opened the back door.

"Mr. Trickett, I think there's somebody following me," Kath spoke breathlessly.

Cutting through the broken railings Philip didn't wait to ask who. Grabbing the chap by the lapels and throwing him against the wooden telegraph pole he shouted, "Is this him cock?"

Timidly, Kath said, "I think so."

"No, no mister, it weren't me," the man denied.

Kath began to panic, thinking it was all in her imagination.

Philip continued to threaten and curse, "I'll bloody kill you ya bastard, if I catch you anywhere near any of my lasses or any of the kids around here, I'll bloody have ya. Have you heard me? And I've clocked ya, so be flaming warned. Now on ya bloody way before I kick ya flaming arse!

Come on Kath, I'll see ya get home all right, cock."

Mr. Trickett's fearless energy came in useful for Kath that night. He was in the right place at the right time, she wouldn't have wished to meet anyone else.

Chapter Nine

Margaret and Kath were academically on equal par, Margaret showing strength in maths, whereas Kath loathed the subject. On the other hand with Kath being the better one at English, this allowed them to help each other with their homework. The two became closer, spending more time together. Carole, Christine and Pat were now working in a factory on the assembly lines, doing mundane jobs, such as building up valves for televisions, or welding little bits of wire together, to go into the valve. They enjoyed work, because every alternate morning and afternoon for a couple of hours, one of the foremen became a D.J. and played the records which the workers had brought in. When any favourite record was selected, all friends would stand up and wave, and all would be reminiscing about the boy of their dreams. The sole intention of the company was to increase productivity, which naturally it did!

This life was not for Pat, she was on a job where she worked all on her own, and so in a way she did not enjoy the same camaraderie that the other girls had. She left the factory and went to work on the switchboard at the local bus company. Margaret and Kath stayed on at school until they were sixteen. Kath was going to be a cadet nurse, whilst Margaret toyed with the idea herself, then changed her mind and went to work in the local bus office. Kath joined the Health Service, but soon became disillusioned with life as cadet nurse; so she left.

The girls were a medley of fifteen and sixteen-years of age, close to reaching maturity. Becoming more grown up meant taking some aspects of life seriously. Thus they found their entertainment on Sunday nights at the Mecca Locarno Ballroom which was to be found at the junction of Yorkshire Street and Centenary Way. This was a central location for young people who sought pleasure in dancing to popular music to come together. Even if one could not dance, one just had to be there or be square. The Mecca attracted teenagers in droves from Burnley and beyond, like pilgrims to worship.

What they wore mattered, the music they listened and danced to was important, but who they were seen with was paramount. Just as a toy appeals to a child, to be accepted by the 'in crowd' had its appeal to the ex-patriots of the youth club. It was the ticket to popularity, the very essence of youth. Young mods queued in all weathers on Sunday evenings from 6:30 p.m. onwards, paying two shillings and sixpence entrance fee, saving one shilling for a coke-a-cola, and one shilling and three pence for the last bus home.

Most females would labour all afternoon polishing fingernails, trimming eyebrows, applying false eyelashes with great precision, curling or sleeking hair, whichever the case might be, then finally modelling the new crepe dress and practising the stance. All of which collectively revealed one's identity, which flavour of fashion one favoured – mod or rocker! Which music most enticed the body to move – the soulful sounds from America, Tamla Motown, Atlantic and Stax, or the hard rock of Cream and Led Zepplin; for all these were essential issues for teenagers of the late 1960's.

The girls in the queue would maintain a 'Twiggy' like pose, with head slightly tilted to one side displaying innocence, their toes slanting inwards like a docile waif. Each had her hands in her pockets, with her vanity case of little purpose, hanging ornamentally from her wrist. Their eyes would peer carefully, seeking out a heartthrob. Competition was tough, like a family of ducks and drakes all scrambling, necks stretching, eager for the same treat.

The boys sought an air of arrogance by applying the same poise as the girls, but the male version having the reverse effect. His highly polished brogue shoes almost reflected the strip of gum he would be chewing. His clean-cut G.I. looks, constituted of very short hair – the crew-cut. This was not an accent on machismo, but instead emphasised the vigour of his coolness, and self-assured attitude. With his hands slipped into his trouser pockets highlighting the fourteen inch vent in the back of his mohair suit jacket. His suit being made from such deluxe fabric was not an indication of his salary either, it was simply considered a mortal sin to be without! One may as well be absent of divine grace as a 'male mod' in the sixties without a mohair suit.

On entrance, the deep sounds of the music evoked emotional rhythm. The boys and girls were transformed as they became 'Sultans of Soul'.

Margaret had earned the complimentary nickname of 'Mamma Cass', (from the Mamas and Papas pop group), as Margaret had the same auburn hair which parted down the middle resembling a pair of rich silk curtains. Since she had taken to following the fashion of the 'mods' her locks had been sheared almost to the skull. The name died, but Margaret's weight stayed, not surprisingly due to her mother cooking steamy hot puddings ladled with thick creamy custard.

There was always a tear-jerker of a story when one of them would have followed her heartthrob around the Mecca ballroom until she was dizzy, only to see him leave the scene with a pretty girl linked to his arm. Some nostalgic soul sound would be playing, which stirred in the pit of the heart. The *Isley Brothers* would be singing, '*I'll guess I'll always love you,*' just as the couple disappeared through the door into the night.

The D.J. spun another record. Margaret had her eye on a group of girls dancing who she thought they ought to imitate. '*Jimmy Mac*' blared around the room, it was her favourite.

"Oh! come on," she called, giving Carole a quick nudge, "I love this". She was singing before she reached the floor.

Their bags were flung into the middle of the swaying dancers, who had now formed a circle. They were swaying with them now.

It felt great to be part of the crowd, thought Margaret. All that was required was to strike up a conversation.

This was where her expertise lay. Having an enquiring mind got the better of her, and she had already done her homework. She had established the short girl in the black shift dress was Jean, who worked as a wages clerk at Lambert & Howarth's Slipper Factory. Margaret was impressed by this status. Snobbery was not one of her attributes, but she had had enough of shop-floor talk from Carole and Christine, who both worked at the Television factory. Jean's position sounded impressive, loading Margaret with yet more curiosity. The girl with short hair the colour of caramel shaping her face, bent down as the music faded to a halt to pick up her bag.

Margaret begged imploringly, "Excuse me will you pass mine whilst you're down there?"

Jean, with her dark brown eyes almost like chocolate buttons, gave a smile; obeying the request she passed the bag to Margaret.

Margaret was an actress! She was straight and to the point with young people she was familiar with. Her tones were sometimes coarse, even rude, but if she was aspiring to meet someone new, her vocal cords altered to become gentler, softer, and much, much quieter, as they filled with persuasive undertones. Her facial expression was one of shyness, just as a timid bird approaching with prudence, yet she was anything but cautionary. This being a useful habit she had acquired over the years. Carole noticed Jean's sallow skin tones, the type that tans easily without much pain or effort.

Margaret continued the amateur dramatics. Smiling whilst speaking, "Hey, do you work with Paul Denson?" Not giving Jean time to answer she continued, "We used to go to Mag's Youth Club with him and his brother Anthony?"

Jean finally spoke, "Yeh! he is a good friend to work with. Has he told you about Thursday nights up at Burco Dean's Working Men's Social Club? They play brilliant music, we go every week. You and your friend here should give it a try. The D.J. is fabulous, he's called Jack Cardale."

Jean obviously loved talking, but unknowingly she had met her match. Sentence by sentence a substantial friendship was being built momentarily. This was Jean's first memory of her friend Margaret.

Jean was cordially invited to join Margaret and Mr. and Mrs. Hand for tea. It was no big deal, for everyone was welcome. Slowly 1, Paisley Street was becoming a refuge centre. Like Kath, Christine and Carole, Margaret's new friend Jean stayed at weekends, if she so wished.

On her first visit Jean was enthralled by the beauty of the garden. Scents of roses, lavender and honeysuckle fragranced the air as she walked down the path. The azure sky was cloudless, as shadows cast the glories of summer. She was taken completely unaware by the astonishing sight. After all, it was merely a council estate address. Her sister Maureen had recently married, and had acquired a similar house on the nearby Stoops Estate. On her visit Jean had passed many exceptional gardens, but they did not compare to this den of enchantment.

Jean's parents had moved into their own property from the Brunshaw Council Estate, in doing so they forfeited a garden. It was of no consequence to them, for her mum and dad showed little interest in such hobbies.

The spanking clean hallway which greeted her on entering the home of her new-found friend made a lasting impression upon her. But what was most inspiring to Jean was the way Margaret's parents turned their attention to their guest. The television set was switched off, not due to the intrusion, but as a welcoming gesture, just a little show of politeness that was habit to this family.

Jean's thoughts quickly returned home. Flashbacks of how blasphemous it was to bring a friend home whilst her parents were indulging in a television programme, passed through her head. Her mother Nora, would drag herself up from the settee and turn up the volume, her dark eyes flashing a look of disgust towards the intruders. Jean quickly composed herself as Mr. Hand sat in his chair wearing a camel-coloured smock, which he wore daily; his legs were outstretched and relaxed.

He started to converse, "So you work as a wages clerk Jean?" he asked, as he puffed on his pipe. His gaze was aimed at the window, rather than directly at the young girl seated on the settee, as if in thoughtful admiration.

Jean simply answered, "Yeh," but her eyes met Mr. Hand's big black boot. Unintentionally she spoke the thought that crossed her mind out loud.

"How come you've got one leg so much shorter than the other, that you have to wear such a big shoe?" Jean felt embarrassed for being too quick in asking such a personal question.

But Mr. Hand was not perturbed, "Eh, lass I got it jumping in the shallow end at Gannow Baths as a boy," he replied with a nod, a wink and another puff of his pipe.

This left her not knowing whether to laugh, or if he was being serious.

Jean was seventeen and a half, the eldest in the group, and this was her first taste of Mr. Hand's good humour. The thought of the elderly gentleman as a young boy plunging into three feet of water, had served to cast her mind back still further, back to the summer evenings of the early fifties.

After school her mum would holler, "Right kids get your swimming tackle ready, we're off to Central Baths."

Jimmy aged eleven years would be the first to ask, "Can I bring Terry, me mate?"

"Ee, course you can," Nora answered, whilst smoking her last cigarette.

She's in a good mood, Maureen thought, who was a couple of years younger than her brother, so she too dared to ask, "What about June, can she come?"

"If you want," came the reply.

Jean said awkwardly, "Well if our Maureen and Jimmy are taking their friends, I want to bring Doreen."

"Okay be quick, go and tell them to get their stuff ready, and make sure they all bring a clean towel."

Before she knew it, Nora had a parade of children accompanying her through Fulledge and up through Finsley Gate to the swimming baths. Boys and girls of all ages, with bubble nylon swimwear wrapped in stripy cotton towels, rolled and tucked under arms followed Nora, as though she was the Pied Piper of Hamelin. She was not at all concerned about taking her own children, and half the neighbourhood's, for this was a getaway from her insipid daily life. She actually enjoyed it.

Jean revelled in the good memory. This memory now felt like fiction, as this was where her mum's hospitality ended. Oh she would offer favours to all and sundry, but to her own children she was maladjusted, displaying only lukewarm affection. Jimmy, Maureen and Jean felt like wild flowers picked, then left without water. They were sweet but uncared-for plants. She dreamed these memories, purely memories.

The table was laid, the meal served, good wholesome roast beef and Yorkshire pudding with healthy vegetables. This was followed by sweet rice pudding, accompanied with strawberry jam. Jean realised the root of Margaret's weight problem, but tucked into the hearty fare all the same. The meal over she offered to side the table and wash up.

"No, no," declined Mrs. Hand, "you sit down love and chat to our Margaret, after all that's what you've come for. Dear me!"

"I'd have to do it at home," explained Jean.

"Well all the same, you sit down love."

Jean's mind drifted back fleetingly to over a decade ago, when she was six-years old, and her younger brother Steven, was born. Bill, Jean's father, was a lone wolf, who did anything for a quiet life. Nora wore the trousers and ruled the roost. Bill obeyed her demands like her lap-dog, while the children cowered like her frightened puppies. His shift at a small local factory on Parliament Street started at 7:30 a.m. Even after a night's sleep his body ached from an old war wound he'd received whilst waiting to be helped off the bloody beaches at Dunkirk.

He suffered a lifetime of disablement for the honour of serving King and Country. There was no sign of braggadocio with Bill, he bore his pain in silence, a trusting silence. He now served as mould injector at Hammonds, making lead soldiers. It was sweaty labour, ladling hot sulphur into moulds. Breathing in the grey dusty air did not help his health.

Nora was frequently insensitive to Bill's needs, but his saving grace was his three-wheeler Robin Reliant car. Saturday mornings he was grateful for his own company; he would put up his sandwiches, fill his thermos flask, organise an old tub full of bait, then drive up to Clowbridge Reservoir and fish all day, enjoying his own secret thoughts.

Once or twice a week he brought a box of lead soldiers home, hoping that Jimmy, Maureen and Jean would have races as to who could remove the most stray ends, thus helping his workload in the factory. The children would bribe Bill.

"Can the winner have a shilling, Dad?" Jimmy would suggest.

"I think that we should all have something," said Maureen, "this is like piece-work."

Poor Billy, scratched his head in wonder!

Nora's fourth child was due mid-August, and prior arrangements had been made for Maureen and Jean to stay at their Auntie Esther's in Colne, until after the birth.

"Don't whinge," snapped Nora to her family, "it won't be for long."

But the only one moaning was poor Jimmy. He would have given his right arm to escape his mother's indelible bossy moods. He was at the butt of her ill-temper on too many occasions. She was like a bulldozer when she started, and a few weeks at Auntie's would have been the buffer he needed. There was no mercy.

"Jimmy you will stay at home like I said," she shouted more impatiently. "Who on earth do you think is going to run to the telephone box and call the midwife if you are not around? You're the eldest and you will stay."

Jimmy's face was as white as alabaster, his mouth dropped, his eyes were as sad as those of a bull-frog.

"And wipe that little boy lost look off your face, or I'll do it for ya!"

Nora hadn't the sincerity to speak lovingly to her offspring even amidst their disappointments. As long as they were clean, fed and watered, she felt her duty done. Warm family atmospheres were meaningless to her. Jimmy stayed to be the messenger boy; the choice wasn't his, but he fulfilled his duty with barely a grudge.

Jean and Maureen each packed an attaché case for their stay at Auntie Esther's. Although Esther had two children of her own, and rooms would have to be shared, the resolution Maureen thought was the best idea her mother had had for a long time. Even at the tender age of eleven Maureen was her mother's housemaid. Washing up was Maureen's chore, ironing was her chore, any order Nora dished out was expected to be carried out almost with obeisance! Maureen began to feel unworthy, and downtrodden, like a thousand grains of sand under footprints, settled for a while only to be washed up by the frothy sea and trodden over and over again.

"Yes!" Maureen thought, "the excitement is all but too much to bear!" She was on a crash course to freedom.

Auntie Esther was piously gentle in nature, possessing a mellowness that her younger sister Nora could only dream of owning. Even at six-years of age Jean was wise to this. She did not need coaxing, just a sudden thought and she could smell her Auntie's kitchen. Country baking was her hobby. Ginger biscuits, fruit cake, and Manchester Tart were just a few of the delectable recipes from her Mrs. Beeton's cookbook. Tending to her family's needs was her pleasure. She sang in raptures while she ironed and starched her girls' pretty dresses. She hummed lullabies while they dozed to sleep.

With a jolt, Jean was brought back to the present. "Are you with us or not?" Margaret asked with a throaty cough.

Mrs. Hand chuckled, "You seem miles away Jean, love."

"Oh, that lovely tea reminded me of the time me and our Maureen went to stay at my Auntie Esther's in Colne. She would not let us do any washing up either. It was so good, when Dad came to collect us after Steven was born, Maureen wouldn't leave. I shouldn't be saying this, but she had all the work to do at home. She stayed for four months." Jean's laugh expressed the lighter side of the dilemma. "My mum's plan had backfired!" Jean explained.

Time passes quickly when you are having fun! If Jean did not get a move on she would miss her last bus home. Fulledge required two buses.

"If I don't leave by ten o'clock I'll turn into a pumpkin!" Jean laughed as she left the happy household.

"Oh be sharp lass, don't you dawdle, or you'll never find your Prince Charming," chuckled Mr. Hand from his chair, amused by his own humour whilst puffing at his pipe.

"Bye and thanks very much for having me," sang Jean, making her way down the path of the enchanted garden.

On the bus gazing absentmindedly out of the window, she thought of the time she had challenged her mother. New clothes had been bought for the annual summer holidays. Jean was delighted with all the new things, but felt that without love it was all a false show, a thin veneer, an imitation of the real tenderness she knew.

"Every year you buy us new clothes for our holidays," Jean continued cautiously, "but what we really all need is a little love."

Nora flounced round in an angry motion and bawled, "Just be careful young lady, you ought to feel lucky that I had *any* of you!"

Jean didn't understand the precise implications of this, but felt as though her mother had given her a necklace of barbed wire. The teenage years served to draw mother and daughter further and further apart. Jean had reached school-leaving age. She had one more dilemma to face concerning Nora. She felt she had been jumping obstacles all her life, but this career discussion would be the final hurdle. The 'eleven plus' examination was intended to cream off the brightest pupils, offering them the choice of Grammar School or Secondary Modern. Once in a while a clever child would slip through the net. Jean, as with Christine, was one such child who failed the examination. At fifteen, she voiced her wishes to sit the G.C.E. 'O' level examinations and hopefully pursue a professional career.

Nora thought the idea absurd, "If you think you're swanning off to school for another twelve months, then off to some college, you're one off! You'll go to Lambert's like me and our Maureen, and like it."

Jean was choked. She did not say a word, but her tears spoke volumes.

In a lighter voice Nora continued, "The trouble with you Jean, is you're above your station, with your head up in the clouds somewhere. Well you can come back down to earth, right now."

Jean cried hot flaming tears and more tears. If sitting at a sewing machine all day, your head down until your neck ached, and to look up was painful, was her mum's philosophy of life, it wasn't hers. Maureen hadn't disputed her mother's plans for her when she left school, she went straight to the factory sewing slippers, and the only reason she saw for work was pay-day.

But Jean wasn't discouraged, she knew she had a good brain and that to waste it would be criminal. Row after row exploded, as more and more tears were shed. She wasn't into martyrdom, nor was she going to be a gofer. But then came the court of appeal and a compromise. Lambert & Howarth's were in need of an Office Junior to train as a wages clerk. Without a word to her mother, Jean applied for the post and was accepted.

Looking down on the factory floor from the elevated glass partitioned room, Jean observed her mother. At a glance she could see a crown of hair, the colour of old gold, dyed to hide the passing years. But disguise can be deceiving, a parting of dark roots with strands of silver threads gave the game away. Jean chuckled to herself as her mother walked through the factory floor, hands in her blue checked overall pockets, and nose turned up in the air, as if **she'd** been promoted. It was all a façade. And why? Well she had a daughter who worked in the office of course! Hypocritical, Jean thought to herself.

After alighting the bus on Lyndhurst Road, Jean turned the key in the varnished door and realised she had relived almost all her tarnished childhood. The outcome was she'd found a haven!

At the same time Mrs. Hand was chunnering to herself, "Looks like I haven't got four daughters, I've now got five!"

Chapter Ten

Many teenage friends passed through Mrs. Hand's living-room, but these five - Kath, Christine, Carole, Jean and of course Margaret, remained as close as caring sisters. All were considered dear enough to be Mrs. Hand's daughters. Each one of the five girls began to show other interests and met individual friends along the way, but they always found some time for each other, so the time-gap from seeing one another, never seemed to exist. It was always as though they had seen each other only the previous week. Other friends were welcome whenever the mood took them, and in this way their social circle expanded, as many other girls found themselves being fussed and pampered by Mrs. Hand whenever they visited Margaret.

There was Anne, an ex-pupil of Miss. Duckworth's, who had enviable grace, like a dragonfly in mid-flight. Veronica was one of the clever girls from St. Mary Magdalene's, who had attended the Grammar School. She was tall and wonderfully wise, forever loyal to her friends, and would cheat on no one. Then there was

Linda, 'purr-fect' but for the notable lack of modesty, and the absence of sincerity towards anyone she met. There was also Pat, small impish and beautifully blonde.

Christine, Pat and their new friend Frances, had fallen madly in love with the Pop Business, and in particular a group called the *'Love Affair'*. They became totally obsessed, following them from town to town, city to city and gig to gig. None of their other friends showed an interest, but on Margaret's sixteenth birthday she and Carole thought they'd give it whirl, just to see what the 'noise' was all about.

The group was playing in Barnsley, which is quite a few miles away from Burnley. The *'Love Affair'* were now known as friends to Christine, Pat and Frances. The girls were all sleeping at Pat's house, whilst her parents were away on holiday. It was the start of Burnley Wake's weeks. Christine's mum had been knitting a blue, angora, fluffy jumper for her to wear, but it was not yet finished. Christine was in a rotten mood because she had nothing new to wear for the trip to Barnsley the following morning. Everyone else was busy washing, ironing or sewing, making the important final touches to their outfits. However Christine was not going to be beaten, she stayed up all night knitting! Click, click, click went the thin long needles, her fingers trying to go faster with each stitch, whilst everyone else slept soundly. By now her mood was softening as she realised that she would finish the beloved garment.

The jumper finally completed and inspected, "Yes," thought Christine, for it looked great, and would be fabulous with the flared, black, crepe trousers she had bought for the gig.

It was too late, or rather to early, to go to bed as the clock had chimed four o'clock, and she had got past tiredness, for she was filled with excitement and anticipation about the day ahead. Barnsley was a very long way and the group would be surprised to see them there.

Margaret was the first person to wake. It was 6:00 a.m. when the sound of the vacuum cleaner broke her sleep. Ninety minutes later Frances came down the stairs, and at 8:15 Pat joined them. Carole did not show her face till 9:30. Showers were taken in the order of rising, and very soon the party left for Barnsley.

Travel arrangements were not on the agenda, the girls would hitchhike, which thankfully was a far less dangerous option then than it is today. Christine, Pat and Frances got into the first mode of transport to stop for them. It was a huge lorry, so they left Margaret and Carole on Rossendale Road with instructions to find the bus station in Wakefield, where they would meet up at 3:00 p.m.

Everything was left to chance, and Margaret and Carole found a better class of transport – a sports car! Luckily the arrangements went to plan, and the five girls opted for the bus for the rest of the way there. Each girl stepped onto the bus without giving a single thought regarding their journey home!

The performance was as excellent as ever, according to the girls, who were able to inform Margaret and Carole such, with them being in the know! They secretly hoped that all five of them would be allowed backstage, if only to show off to Margaret and Carole. They were, and Nick, who was the road-manager for the group, set his cap at Christine. Of course she only had eyes for Mick in the group, but she went along with the lad's flattery, if only to obtain a lift home. When he asked, Nick did not realise how far he would have to travel to take Christine home.

"Yes," she answered, fluttering her eyelashes, and smiling at him, "if you will also take my friends."

Nick agreed that he would, "Three will have to sit in the back of the van with the equipment though."

"That's absolutely fine," Christine assured him, but still intentionally forgot to say where she lived, or to give any regard for her friends squashed between a bass drum, guitars and amplifiers in the back. "Keep driving straight on, yes that's right, oh it's a lot further yet." Christine informed Nick.

Nick asked her, "Will you come to London with me?"

"Wow!" Christine could not believe her luck. "Frances and Pat could also go with them, and they could go to the next gig which was in Hampshire the following night," her thoughts raced on.

When Nick realised that Christine lived further away than he first thought, he took the girls for a fish and chip supper. The delicious smell drifted into the back of the van, which was dark and dreary as no light passed through.

As they approached the outskirts of Burnley, the van was pulled over to the side of the road by the police, who wanted to know what was contained in the back? The constable asked lots of questions, such as who was who, and where had they been to and where they were going? Flashes appeared before Christine of what her dad would say if he knew, or how the police would react if they saw the three girls squashed in the back. She had been banned several times from following the group, for she was forever coming home late, or not at all, having secretly stayed at Frances's house. Thankfully the policeman was satisfied with the answers which Nick provided to his questions, and they were allowed to drive on. Now relieved, Christine began to relax again and look forward to the trip to London.

When they reached Burnley the girls had to report to the Trickett house to inform Philip that they were home safe and sound from the alleged trip to Blackpool, which had been their decoy story. Christine shouted up the stairs that they would not be around the following day, as they were going to Morecambe, which was of course another lie!

Margaret and Carole were safely dropped off at Pat's house, whilst the other three made their way to Frances's house, where they all crashed down on the settees and slept for a few hours before driving all the way to London.

During the journey down to the Capital, Nick informed the girls that there would be a party after the gig, which was being given by a famous producer, and other stars would be there. So although he had fancied his chances with Christine initially, he was now getting the message that he was wasting his time, as she only had eyes for Mick.

"I'll take you to the party," Nick suggested, "but when we get there, it's everyone for themselves. In other words, I will be looking for someone to take home, and I'll leave you to yourself. Is that okay?"

"Sure is," smirked Christine, for this was just what she wanted, and it had just come about without any grief. In fact she had been thinking how she could lose Nick once they arrived in Hampshire?

The girls were taken to a mansion owned by some rich and famous pop manager. It was out in the open countryside of one of the shires. A parade of cars followed one another to a secluded house hidden by a long driveway lined by extensive trees. Upon entering, it was Mick who approached Christine, totally amazed that she was at this party, which was so far away from Burnley. He wondered how on earth she had managed to be invited, because the people attending had been selected personally by the host. She explained that she had been invited by Nick, who could now be seen nearly eating a 'hippie-type' female, who wore a long flowing dress with several layers of beads around her neck.

Christine felt rather lost in the crowded house, and was aware she was out of her depths amongst the hazy smoke. She herself had consumed too much alcohol. Whilst searching for her friends in the early morning light she found her heartthrob Mick, with his long-term girlfriend. Realising Pat and Frances had left she felt alone with complete strangers. After desperately gathering her thoughts, she asked a soberly man to take her to the nearest police station, as she needed to be homeward-bound. This whole experience was the end of her dream to be a pop star's wife.

The police in London informed her parents via the police in Burnley. She was kept in a cold cell, which had a strong stench of stagnant urine. She was put on a train at Euston the following morning. All the while the train was trudging northwards she fingered her muslin floral dress that resembled night-wear, as opposed to day-wear, and wondered what fate awaited her at home?

"Oh what the hell," thought Christine, "she would get murdered from her dad, but it was worth it." Her only concern on her journey home was that she hoped both Pat and Frances would get to know that she was on her way home, and that they too would get home safely.

The first stop was at Mrs. Hand's house to find out how the land lay, for she could always be relied upon in any hour of need.

"Oh, Christine love, you are in a great deal of trouble with your dad. Carole was down here with our Margaret and your Stephen had to bring her home. He said that the police had been to the house and he wanted Carole to do some explaining."

Christine expected something like this, so she just asked for a cup of tea and a cardigan to wear over the flimsy, see through dress.

Christine walked slowly home from Margaret's but when she entered the house she was in for a shock. Not only did she get called all the names under the sun, and told that she would not be going out for a whole month, but she was physically attacked by her father. She got the beating she had expected, whilst Audrey pleaded with him to stop.

Carole also tried to pull Phil away, but he just got angrier. This was on account that Christine said she would not tell him where she had been, and she simply crouched on the floor, hands over her head, in order to protect herself, and waited for him to stop. The final touch was a kick in the backside, that knocked her into the stairway, behind the front door, where she hit her head on the adjoining wall. Then it was finally over! Christine went up to her bed, where she buried herself underneath the covers.

Phil then shouted at Audrey and Carole, trying to blame them for what he had just done to his daughter, as he was now full of regret. Completely without the gumption to say sorry, he went to the pub to drown his sorrows.

Later that night, Carole crawled into bed besides Christine and told her not to worry, he was a bastard and he would get his comeuppance. Christine talked over the party and events with Carole, and soon forgot about her aches and pains. Pat and Frances had both arrived home safely, and had been warned not to call for Christine whilst her dad was still furious. Carole became the messenger for the girls, so they could keep in touch.

When Christine did go out again she first went to the fairground with Margaret, Carole and Kath, as her dad had banned her from seeing Pat and Frances. They all met up that night, and Phil was unaware that Audrey had allowed Christine out whilst he was at the pub, provided that she would be home long before he was.

Chapter Eleven

The social circle expanded not only with the introduction of new people, but because they were not content with the local scene. It was not that they disliked Burnley, but it is one hundred percent perfectly true *'the more you have the more you want'*. This troop of girls was no exception to this rule. They would travel to Bolton's Cromwellian Club, Manchester's Rowntree Spring Gardens, or The Island Room at Blackpool Mecca. They also ventured to the Stax Club at Blackburn, but Accrington Conservative Club, or Accy Con Club as it was referred to, always held the highest stakes. This was all because Jean was madly in love with Kevin McKoffrey.

Make-up applied and dressed to impress, the girls would board the train at Burnley Barracks Station – a compromise of convenience. Moving from carriage to carriage, hoping to dodge the inspector, and equally so dodge the fares, they soon became successful at mastering this little trick. But there was an art to it all. Their make-up and aptitude had to guarantee them entrance to the club, be a hyssop to the boys, plus provoke pure green envy from the other girls.

On the bus home the roles were set in reverse gear. Only affording half fare, the seventeen-year old girls were now sweet sixteen, never been kissed and employing an orchestra of innocent voices.

"Burnley please, half fare! Thank you," all said in the same breath.

The driver, on his last run of his shift, was too tired to attempt an argument, so simply resigned himself to the clubbers' requests.

Often, without much thought of dire consequences. they would stick out a thumb, and maybe even a leg, to hitch a lift to further destinations. It was a case of anything, in order to dig the social scene.

The Lodestar at Ribchester was yet another favourite. One Friday night Kath, Christine, Jean, Margaret and Carole decided to make such a trip which was twenty miles or so from their home town. They had walked to Padiham, which is about two miles away, as the crow flies, without any luck. At the top of the town Kath gave a glimpse of a smile to a passing motorist, whilst her right thumb glided in the evening midsummer air. A Bohemian sort of chap stopped his Rover car; Kath hurriedly beckoned the rest of the hikers.

"We've got a lift girls, come on quickly," she urged them.

"I've only stopped to go to the fish and chip shop," said the friendly man, astounded by this group of girls.

But it was too late, seated, smiling, and as pleased as punch at their success, the girls settled down for their trip to Ribchester. Amazingly, the poor gentleman felt obliged to take his passengers to their destination. He drove in bewilderment at first to the Roman Village of Ribchester, but was quite chatty by the time they arrived.

The girls muttered many words of "Thanks very much."

Kath even joked and said, "See you next Friday."

He reversed his car and drove back to purchase fish and chips to take home to his wife.

Chapter Twelve

Whilst visiting another youth club, Margaret was intrigued by two girls who both shared the name, Linda. These two girls glowed with confidence and appeared far more worldly-wise than any of the friends, and so Margaret introduced them into the circle. One of the Linda's, although not a natural blonde, had hair which complemented her clear blue eyes and milky-white complexion. She was immaculately presented and pristine; her voice gave her an air of arrogance. Linda was not a *'what you see, is what you get'* sort of person, she thrived on promiscuity. Jean even thought that promiscuity had been invented for this girl.

Naturally Linda was always popular with the male species, which left the girls quietly envious. She had been well aware of her sexuality from an early age, so flaunted herself in the presence of the boys at every given opportunity. This gave her an advantage over the other girls, as she used it to increase her popularity, thus labelling herself as an easy target.

Monday night was Mrs. Hand's regular visit to see her friend Elsie, whilst Mr. Hand enjoyed a quiet drink in the Clarion Club, leaving the house free for the girls to meet up and gossip there. Linda, who lived not far from Margaret, was invited to join the gathering on Monday nights. It quickly turned into 'confession night' as she disclosed what she had been up to over the weekend. This was perfect, because she would always have had a couple of dates. Everyone would confess who they had met Friday, Saturday or Sunday, but all apart from Linda were novices when it came to the opposite sex. They were good Catholic girls, whereas Linda believed in the new trend of 'free love'. She captivated her audience, as they were totally enthralled with her tales, and could not believe her revelations.

Mrs. Hand's tall-backed chair was occupied by the storyteller, whilst the rest of the girls shared the settee, or were sprawled on the floor around her feet listening with baited breath. Once she had started, she was wedged in a kind of cul-de-sac.

The girls would unwittingly ask awkward questions like, "If he had a car? Where did you go?"

Linda would answer proudly, "To Crown Point, where do you think!"

There would be gasps of horror from around the room. The cheekiest would remark rudely, "Come on then, if you touched it what did it feel like?"

Linda enjoyed spilling out the graphic details, which were followed by more sighs of disgust and hands covering faces. Linda was at the girls' peril, without realising she was earning herself a lewd reputation - one without honour, but she enjoyed the sweet flavour of life, and was a creature of passion.

The boys thought of her as a launching pad for their sexual desires. As for the girls, Linda taught them the basic facts of life on confession nights, and for that they were always grateful!

What was annoying about Linda though was that she held herself in such high regard. She believed she had impeccable morals and stated every week, "My mother was a virgin when she married."

The girls would just mock her to themselves, or whenever Linda was not present saying, "You most certainly do not take after your mother!"

The five friends often found themselves harboured at Margaret's home, but Jean in particular loved to chatter.

Mrs. Hand would speak up, "Where are you thinking of going tonight love?"

"Oh, I don't know, Burco Dean's probably, we didn't go there last week, we caught the train to Accrington instead, but we can't miss twice in a row, we've got to keep up with what's happening, you know," Jean answered, smiling while relaying the information.

Once outside, Margaret, somewhat annoyed asked, "What do you have to tell them everything for?"

Jean replied perfectly honestly, "Because Margaret, your parents take an interest in what we do, and where we go, as well as who with. Mine have never asked me what I do; you're really lucky."

Margaret did not comment, just cast her eyes downwards towards her feet, with eyes set wide in appreciation, and realisation of her mum and dad's parenting skills.

But typically Margaret understood Jean's parents much better than Jean did herself. She'd treated Mrs. Macro like a blank canvas, on which she painted her own rosy picture with her inquisitive personality. The hardened mother warmed to Jean's new friend welcoming her into their home. Her reward was that only Margaret could stay. This they used to their own advantage, when very late one Saturday night (or rather early Sunday morning) they became a little unstuck. They'd danced the night away at the Cromwellion Club in Bolton. Having been offered a lift home by a local lad in a transit van, they'd no worries about getting home. Five girls plus Keith and Andy all disembarked at Margaret's front gate after a very bumpy ride.

"Are you all staying here?" Keith asked.

"Not likely," Margaret answered, "Where are we all going to sleep?"

She hadn't a care in the world, but Carole, Linda and Veronica knew that they couldn't go home at 2:00 a.m. or there'd be trouble. All parents had been told their girls were staying at 1, Paisley Street, which wasn't a problem for anyone.

"None of us can go home. What are we going to do?" announced a rather scared Carole.

Jean came up with the solution, "Margaret can come home with me; so you lot stay here." She laughed as though she was joking.

The boys laughed too!

"You can't do that, what will your parents say in the morning?" said Andy astounded.

Margaret took great delight in telling them only she could stay at Jean's.

Decision made, Margaret handed over her key to Carole. "Here, creep in, take you shoes off, and leave your tights on the kitchen sink, me mum will know you're in, and in the morning she'll wash them for you ready for the Mecca tomorrow night. These two will give us a lift to Jean's, won't you lads?"

Keith and Andy felt obliged as Veronica, Linda and Carole sneaked their way into Margaret's double bed.

Mrs. Hand rose at 7:30 that Sunday morning, but there was nothing unusual about that. After putting the kettle on she rinsed the tights through and hung them out on the line to dry. "Looks like she brought two home," she said as she wondered which ones?

At 9:00 a.m. she set the tray with four mugs of coffee and a plate of digestive biscuits, then climbed the stairs. Three heads peeped from under the eiderdown as she placed the tray on the bedside table.

Three faces smiled quietly whilst saying, "Thank you."

"Where's our Margaret?" asked Mrs. Hand with concern in her voice.

"Oh, we're sorry Mrs. Hand," said Carole. "We all came home together, but there wasn't enough room for five of us, so she's gone to stay at Jean's. Margaret said that you wouldn't mind."

"Oh, I don't love, as long as she's all right."

"She is Mrs. Hand," Veronica assured her quickly. "Jean's mum and dad won't allow anyone else to stay, so we thought it was the best thing to do."

"All right, now you drink ya coffee before it goes cold, and your tights will be ready for tonight, they're blowing on the line."

As this good lady left the room the three of them breathed a sigh of relief.

Handing Leonard his mug, Mrs. Hand mumbled, "Well there's three lasses in there, but not one of 'em is our Margaret!"

"Where is she then?" he asked.

"At Jean's," his wife answered in amazement.

Propped up on his pillows Mr. Hand just sat chuckling as his good humour came to the fore.

Chapter Thirteen

January 1970 started brisk, wild and very cold. Margaret, Jean, Carole and Linda leaned towards booking their first summer holiday together. Three of them had to take extra part-time jobs as silver service waitresses at the Keirby Hotel in Burnley to help pay the £23.00 costs to Spain for two weeks.

They scanned brochure after brochure, examining resorts, hotels and the facilities they offered in an excitatory fashion. After much deliberation, Hotel Clipper at Lloret de Mar won the day, but unfortunately the flight was scheduled for early evening from Ringway in Manchester direct to Barcelona, thus requiring a lunch-time finish from work on Friday. This was quite feasible for Carole and Jean, however Margaret and Linda's managers were reluctant to allow such flexibility.

After careful reconsideration the Hotel Villa in Calella appeared to be a more suitable option. Though lacking a swimming pool was the hotel's negative aspect, Margaret pointed out that it had a restaurant open to the public, and so the food was bound to be particularly good! All were now in agreement, so the holiday was booked for the first two weeks in July, the Burnley Wake's fortnight.

The flight was scheduled for 22:00 hours on Friday evening, which suited all concerned. Jean's driving instructor, Mr. Morris, had a reliable Hillman Imp car, and offered to drive the four holiday-makers to Manchester Airport. Carole was the last to be picked up from Harold Avenue, and neighbours waved enviably from their doorways as her dad carried her luggage out as if he was her own private bellboy. This in itself was previously unheard of.

When she squeezed herself in between Margaret and Linda in the back seat, Carole realised that she was the butt of their laughter. Three of them wore clothes of a casual nature for comfort, trousers or jeans, sweaters and macs. Even Linda, who prided herself on her *haute couture* style was dressed informally, but Carole was dressed as though she had earned her wings for flying.

"Where do you think you're going dressed like that?" Margaret laughed out loud.

"To the airport where do you think," Carole snapped back at her.

"I would have thought that you would have put your jeans on," Linda joined in, "you won't be comfortable like that!"

Margaret still laughing announced, "She always wanted to be an air-hostess."

Carole had chosen her dark brown twill, skirt suit, cream and brown shoes, that had cost her £7.00 from Holts. This was a whole week's wage! A lemon cravat at her neck, matching stud earrings and pale lemon gloves completed the outfit. Naturally she held her beloved vanity case to carry her make-up. On arrival at Manchester Airport she fell almost flat on her face, aware that only the cabin crew adorned such style. Couples, families, parties of teenage boys and girls were sat or lay anywhere they could find an unoccupied space. Flights had been unexpectedly delayed. The airport lounge looked as though it was housing five hundred refugees, all casually clothed. Carole felt very much overdressed, but uncharacteristically she strutted around like a peacock displaying his lustrous plumage.

The prospects of boarding the aircraft sent bubbles of excitement fizzing to the brim, yet the chums all felt the conquest of fear. Once seated, the engines revved, rousing a genuine mixture of emotional energy.

Arriving at Barcelona in the early hours of Saturday morning they boarded a coach after recovering their luggage from the carousel. The vehicle made its way to several resorts with only the diamond-studded stars and a crescent of a moon to torch the sky. Winding roads took a crooked course to Calella. The holiday town remained a mysterious secret until mid-morning when the girls' batteries had been recharged by temporal sleep.

Hotel Villa was a small but friendly, individual hotel, offering warm and professional hospitality. Being located just a stride away from the transparent sea, and the sandy seashore resembling golden crystallised sugar, more than compensated for its absence of a swimming pool.

Late Saturday morning they set off to investigate and find their bearings. At their very first steps outside the hotel their bodies absorbed the heat that felt alien, but the air was perfumed with the sweet smell of warm dough and unfamiliar spices. Sitting at a beach bar they admired nature's embroidery, richly combining man-made parasols, and even the Spanish waiter who flaunted his culture and language. This new experience was all part of life's rich tapestry, finely interwoven to create an ambience of pleasure.

Coca-colas were placed on the table, as the waiter spoke in broken English aided by sign language, waving his metal tray in one hand and his note pad in the other, indicating a large bird or an aeroplane.

"Bang, bang!" he shouted pointing to the beautiful mountain range behind, filled with luscious vegetation which lined its slopes adding glamour to its existence.

"Aeroplane – crash – English people killed, last night!" He shouted with realistic fear in his voice.

Gasps of disbelief came from the girls but Margaret was adamant it wasn't true. "Take no notice, he's trying to frighten us, don't even look at him," she sulked, turning away in utter disgust.

But Jean already had her camera out, giving him instructions for a photo call.

Margaret would not budge, she hadn't come to Spain to listen to horror stories. She sat poised, her dark sunglasses partially hiding her displeasure; with drink in hand, all the while bearing a likeness to her Royal Highness Princess Margaret cruising on her yacht in the Caribbean.

The waiter's claims were dismissed in a cautionary manner by Carole, Jean and Linda uncertain whether to be happy or sad.

The following morning whilst browsing at a kiosk, the tragic headlines hit all four of them face on. Photographs of families they all knew appeared on the front pages of the tabloid press.

"British Holidaymakers Perish in Spanish Air Disaster!"

The bold print was unmistakable. Jean purchased a newspaper. The early Friday evening flight from Manchester to Barcelona had crashed into the Pyrennees Mountains killing over two hundred passengers and crew. This was the reason for the delay coming out to Spain. This was the flight the girls could not make because of their working arrangements.

On reflection Margaret announced sombrely, "It wasn't our turn to go!"

Each one agreed, shedding tears, weeping for neighbours, townsfolk and acquaintances. The glorious mountains were psychotic. They'd become a deep pit, a black hole, a crematorium for ordinary families who had saved vigorously all year round for the holiday in Spain, now never to return to their homeland. The girls all felt a desperate urge to hear their parents' voices, in order to let them know that they were safe, but none of their parents possessed a telephone. Each girl sent a postcard marked urgent, which miraculously found their way to the appropriate address promptly.

Three days before the end of their holiday they were sat enjoying breakfast when the waiter handed both Carole and Margaret letters from home.

Carole fought hard to hold back her tears when she read of how both her mum and dad said, "We have all missed you, and can't wait for you to come home." She realised the emotional strain they must have felt on hearing the shocking news of the air crash.

Margaret read her letter with more dignity. Mrs. Hand had put together a rescue package. She had the means to finance the four girls home via overland and had written offering to do just that, sensing the anxiety they would be going through worrying about the flights back home. Margaret felt it wise to decline the offer. She felt that if they did not take the flight back to Manchester they may never fly again.

They boarded the plane late into the night with mixed feelings. A longing for home and the dread of the journey, leaving sombre moods all around the aircraft.

Back home in Burnley, families, friends, neighbours and communities became shock absorbers, cushioning each other from the grief and pain. Memorial services were held locally to commemorate those people who had lost their lives so tragically. May they rest in peace!

Chapter Fourteen

With the passage of time the special years drew to a close far too early, but the links of friendship continued to interweave. Real comrades last forever, but need not always live in each other's pockets. Sometimes several hundred miles separated them from one season to another, but thoughts in hearts and minds ensured that they were always there for one another.

Christine was the first to meet her first real love Peter. He wasn't rich or famous, but master of the dance floor; she was smitten by his talent, his equipoise and his Mr. Cool swagger. She herself had developed into a graceful creature, even winning local beauty pageants. Never being content at Mullards factory, sat all day making valves for television sets, she craved glamour. Peter slipping and sliding on the dance floor provided a hint of that. Settling into courtship lessened slightly the desire for a life full of thrills and fancies. However she still had her dreams.

For her and Peter as a couple, she dreamt of a life in Canada. Jeanette Wolstencroft who was a friend to both

Carole and Christine, had emigrated there with her family, when they were still at St. Hilda's school, and often Christine would think and wonder what her life was like now she lived what seemed to be a million miles away?

Chris McCormack, a childhood friend of Peter's, had emigrated a number of years earlier, and was visiting family and friends in Burnley. They met up with him and he painted a rose-coloured picture, which enticed Christine and Peter to dwell on dreams of a new and exciting life on the other side of the Atlantic. For herself, nurse training, or even midwifery would fulfil her ambitions.

"Well you can dream," she would say, "they can't take away your dreams."

She breezed in and out of these fanciful thoughts. Then horror struck, six weeks before Christmas 1971 her ideological vision for the future melted like summer snow. She was pregnant!

Announcing her predicament to Audrey her mother, was easy compared to the confrontation she knew that she would have to endure from Philip, her father. She knew that he would be so cross and milk the whole episode. But who could blame him? He wanted a better start in married life for his daughter than he and Audrey had had. Musing at work she pondered over the sorry state of affairs. She had to decide which time of day reflected his most even temper. He worked nights at the paper mill and so early morning was out of the question. He would be exhausted after a long shift, besides she needed Peter there as her support and ally, for he was her defence mechanism.

The moment may have appeared untimely, but when Christine saw her father stood at the pot kitchen sink, swilling his face with cold water, it seemed to give her and Peter an advantage. They hoped the splashes would act as a smoke screen defusing both their embarrassment and guilt. Philip did a double take as Christine meekly spoke.

"Dad I've got something to tell you. Me and Peter want to get married, I'm expecting a baby."

"What the bloody hell – Audrey did you know all about this, it's all your bloody fault. I knew we shouldn't have let them go to Newquay on that bloody holiday. How on earth am I supposed to pay for **two** bloody weddings?" He swung around, dabbing his face with the towel and nearly exploding out of his cream string vest. His only words to Peter were, "I haven't got a bloody carrot!" His face became as red as home-grown beetroot, as he grew hot with rage.

Christine and Peter numbly moved back towards the kitchen table, for fear he would strike out.

Audrey hovered pathetically at the kitchen door, "Don't Phil, don't hit her she's having a baby," her words sounding desperate.

"I'm not a simpleton. I know she's having a bloody baby. Now get out of my sight the lot of you," Phil ordered.

As these words rang out, Alan, Carole's fiancé, knocked on the front door. Phil was just about to straddle the stairs. Opening the door, he picked Alan up by his lapels, gripping so tightly, that the young lad's feet left the floor.

"I hope you haven't come to tell me she's in the same state as her sister," his voice sounding as loud and gruesome as ever.

Christine had rehearsed her lines over and over again, she did not need an understudy. But what she didn't expect was for Alan to walk in and be ambushed, he looked as though he had been taken hostage.

"Out the bloody lot of you," her father screamed.

The two young couples didn't need telling twice; grabbing their coats they made their way out of the house into the cold winter air, and headed for the local pub opposite the cemetery – The Griffin Hotel. They were grateful for the wind which lowered the temperature somewhat for it had been far too hot and clammy in the house. The four of them sat in the snug now, grateful for the fading embers in the fire-grate opposite. They were all thankful that they could stay until Phil had left to start his night shift at the paper mill. They would be only too pleased to be up early for work the following morning before he arrived home.

Peter and Alan's pints of mild, Christine's half of lager and Carole's Britvic orange lasted all night, as if they were already on enforcement rations. Money was always in short supply, but especially so now as they were all saving up to get married.

Carole had met Alan in September 1970; the encounter had materialised itself as a comic opera. She had been invited to a friend's 18th birthday party in Padiham. A local lad called Mick walked her home and arranged to meet her the following evening – Sunday inside the Mecca. She looked forward to this second date, but then Alan Hawke made his appearance as though he was doing a dare.

"Er, Mick's no money, he's not coming, so I'm here instead," he declared.

Carole had to admire his cheek. Wondrously the courtship blossomed.

One night whilst sheltering from the rain in a doorway in the Duke Bar area of town, he whispered in her ear, "Let's get married."

Carole agreed, not because she was passionately in love, but on the account of Alan's ability to make her laugh. She had her own recipe for a happy marriage; one of the main ingredients was a large helping of good humour. Of course there were other essentials, but all other components could grow like a sweet cake rising in a warm oven.

They were buying a small two-bedroomed, quasi-semi-detached house in Caernarvon Avenue, near the Palace House estate. A date had been set for Easter Monday, April 3rd 1972 for their wedding at St. Mary Magdalene's Church. Saving had become their priority and their lives, but Phil, her dad, being a man of pride, wanted to pay his way, following the normal tradition of the bride's father. Now Christine was making plans, and taking the fast track to marriage, Phil felt bewildered, and thoroughly bogged down with the pressure of being the father of daughters.

For a full week Philip sulked. They endured seven days of silent meals, like a period of mourning.

"Tell your dad his tea is ready," Audrey would pass on to any of the children.

"Tell her I don't want it," he'd snap back, both within earshot of each other.

Then the following Friday teatime, he walked into the living-room and announced proudly, "I've been measured up for a new suit and ordered it for the wedding."

He had come out of his doleful sorrow and took an earnest interest in the proposed wedding plans. It was as though a dark, shady veil had been lifted. Life was no longer a murky river, he could see his way forward. Working all the overtime that was offered, he found the money for two weddings. January 22nd 1972 was the date set for Christine and Peter's ceremony at the family's parish church – St. Mary Magdalene's. Everyone rallied round, saving green-shield stamps for household necessities. Pots and pans, towels and bedding bales were all acquired through the green-shield stamp collection.

One week before the wedding, the traditional Hen Party had been arranged, which would be a joint event teamed up with Jean's 21st birthday party. The girls had organised a coach to take them and twenty or so more friends to the Bier Keller at Manchester. It would be a great night, for nearly everyone there was celebrating something. Of course, you had to have a taste for beer, which was served in three-pint jugs, the more that was swilled down, the more the Umpha Band encouraged the singing and dancing. A favourite was *'The Dam Busters'* which was a chorus from *'I am the Music Man'*, and always guaranteed to raise the roof and entice the party revellers to dance on the table, including a pregnant Christine and a rather merry Jean. Carole, ever the worrier, was trying her best to get Christine down because of her condition, but Christine only wanted to dance nearer to the flashing neon lights for just the one song, much to Carole's relief.

At one point Christine was quite worried about Kath who was incessantly sick in the ladies' toilets. It appeared that Kath was in a state quite beyond reasoning and was not fully orientated with her surroundings. Thinking it a good idea at the time, Christine struggled, but managed to find Kath a place of safety by tying her waist-length hair around the taps of the sink and thus leaving Kath prisoner, whilst she went back to find the others. Margaret wanted to know where Kath was?

Christine assured her that Kath was fine, and confidently said, "Come and look what I've done, she's not going anywhere!"

They quickly proceeded to the ladies' toilets and found their friend, who was now being sick in the hand basin, unable to move.

Margaret was horrified and firmly shouted, "Christine what have you done," in her authoritative voice. "Are you trying to choke her? Get her undone now!"

Christine just stood there oblivious to what she had done.

Margaret continued to shout at Kath, "How have you managed to get yourself into this state? You know you can't keep up drink for drink with us."

After being released by Margaret, Kath, who had now found her second wind, swilled her face, combed her hair and slipped back into the party mode. Soon it was time to go home, and it was a small wonder that all the girls who came on the coach made it back at the end of the night.

There was also a Stag Party with some familiar faces from Burnley Mecca. The partygoers lived in Bolton, but one of them had missed his bus, so he travelled home with the girls.

After two months of reception planning, reserving taxis, ordering the wedding cake, booking the photographer and sewing bridesmaids' dresses, the big day dawned cold but crisp. Philip was as much aglow with nervous energy as Christine. He put on a performance. Floundering a little with the stereogram as he was out of his domain with such equipment, but nevertheless he placed the vinyl record on the turntable, and turned the volume up to the highest decibel, so that the strains of *'The Wedding'*, echoed up the stairs. Phil gingerly carried Christine's breakfast upstairs on a tray, and demanded that she enjoy both her food and the music. This sort of hospitality was a new experience for Philip, but he took glory in bestowing such affection on his beautiful daughter on her wedding morning.

Christine arrived at the church with her father who was beaming like a newly polished Toby jug. His new grey suit did him justice, for he was still exceedingly handsome. The bride looked resplendent in her white satin dress, wreath and veil. The image of a dazzling snow queen walked up the left-hand aisle of St. Mary Magdalene's Church to meet Peter, her bridegroom, and Father Fraher at the altar. They took their wedding vows with seventy-five guests as witnesses, and made their home on the same council estate as her parents, until a mortgage could be obtained for their own property.

Justin Marc was born after a long punishing labour resulting in a vacuum suction delivery. Peter was ordered to remain outside the clinical area.

The midwife announced the birth of his son but said, "I do hope you realise how brave your young wife has been in there?"

He as ushered into the room to be with mother and baby, but not for long, as Justin was admitted to the Special Care Baby Unit because of his traumatic birth. The event had left his face the colour and texture of raspberry coulis. His carrot red hair distinguished him from all the other new-born babies in the nursery. His date of birth was July 7th 1972. He therefore shared both Margaret's 19th birthday and his Nana and Grandad's 21st Wedding Anniversary. Margaret felt privileged to hear the news on her special day, but felt a certain amount of common empathy.

Burnley wake's weeks were the first fortnight in July, which meant frequently friends and family would be enjoying themselves on holiday, unfortunately missing birthday parties. Margaret gave Christine and Peter strict instructions to celebrate Justin's birthday on the day, but provide a party immediately after the second week in July. That was Margaret laying down the law. Justin grew into a bright toddler, clever enough to read at three years of age, thanks to the dedication of his young parents.

The same year, at the same church, Carole married Alan amid flurries of April snow. Within fifteen months the couple became a family when they produced their first-born, a daughter, Keelie Jayne, who arrived into the world on June 23rd 1973. She was the image of her daddy, with her mop of black fluffy hair, and eyes that were to be her fortune, for they were bluer than the sky on a cool cloudless day.

The birth had caught Carole and Alan quite unawares. June 22nd was a hot Friday, with her due date being the 24th June Carole felt it safe to make her way down to Burnley Centre by bus to wander around the shops. She had already made arrangements to meet Alan at 5:00 p.m. after his work at the Corporation. Whilst window gazing she met Mrs. Hand on St. James' Street.

"Hey, love what are you doing down here, you should be at home with your feet up," she stated feeling rather concerned.

"I'm thinking of going up to Mereclough to the hairdressers," Carole replied, a little uncertainly, "my hair is driving me mad. I'll have to have it cut before the baby comes."

"Well lass," Mrs. Hand said, "you haven't got long, it's make up your mind time."

At that Carole made an instant decision and took the bus to the beautiful bungalow where a hairdresser worked from her home, three miles out of town. Her tummy ached whilst Marilyn kneaded her head under running water. Her hair was cut short into a style without fuss.

An hour later she made her way to the bus shelter on the opposite side of the road. Whilst standing there she felt some discomfort, but not alarm. Within two minutes a small white van pulled up, and the driver asked where she was going?

"I'm going to Burnley Centre – the bus station," Carole answered.

"Well love, I'd like to give you a lift, you've got two hours to wait for the next bus. Look I've got my young daughter with me in the back. I'll take you wherever you need to go. You certainly can't wait here in your condition."

Carole took him at his word, and he drove her to meet Alan. Whilst leaning on the trolley to ease the dragging feeling in her tummy, together they bought groceries from Moneysave the supermarket. They boarded the double-decker bus to Caernarvon Avenue on the other side of town.

It was a beautiful evening, the sky hinting at 'Shepherds Delight'. Although Carole felt out of sorts, they took a stroll around Lowerhouse Lodge – a local beauty spot. Linked arm in arm with Alan, Carole suddenly stooped and doubled up in pain. Pains were arriving every five minutes now. They were back home at ten minutes to nine. It was obvious that the time had come for Carole to be admitted into the hospital.

Keelie Jayne was born in the early hours of Saturday morning. It was a relatively normal birth; even so Carole felt her body had been given an electric shock. Her new haircut stood up on end, remaining so for the next six weeks. Alan took a taxi home from Edith Watson Maternity Unit at 3:30 a.m. but he didn't go to bed, instead he just sat in wondrous awe at the miracle of love and life.

Fifteen Chapter

Whilst Christine and Carole settled down to married life and motherhood, Margaret, Kath and Jean sought excitement through working in hotels on the Isle of Wight. A jungle of colourful horticulture, blending with seaside memorabilia met Margaret, Jean and Kath when they arrived there. Delphiniums stretched to reach the overhanging thatch of the ridges of the tiny cottages. Clumps of Red Hot Pokers stood guard with their proud tufts of yellow and flaming red. A carpet of purple Rambling Sailors wove its way in the foregrounds of country gardens, making each village a picture worthy of sitting on top of a chocolate box. The seaside resorts were charming, locked in a retained period of Punch and Judy shows, donkey rides, pirate ships and barrel organs singing out *'The sailor's hornpipe'* and other seaside shanties.

Margaret and Jean worked as waitresses in the White City Holiday Apartments in Sandown, whereas Kath and a girl who lived in Padiham called Hilary, worked as chambermaids in a hotel in Shanklin. Whilst there Kath kept in touch with Margaret and Jean, but they did not really socialise much owing to distance and the lack of time off work. The girls enjoyed the freedom from family restrictions, and felt like they had suddenly grown up. They were able to choose what time to come in at night and where to go.

Kath began to smoke, so when she did meet up with the girls, Margaret insisted that she teach her this new habit, in order to appear more sophisticated, or so she thought. Margaret really enjoyed smoking, and sometimes smoked brightly coloured cigarettes which came in a fancy package. She thought that these looked so elegant.

The work here was hard and tiresome, because the girls and boys who had gone over to the Isle of Wight for the seasonal work, constantly burned the candle at both ends. They would have to serve breakfast to the holiday-makers, then later serve in the self-service café throughout the day. It was only natural that they wanted some fun after their long day's work. They were given time off in the afternoon and two nights a week, but they wanted to have it all. They often slept during the afternoon, though it was not a very relaxed sleep, as they had a head full of rollers, hoping to look better than they would feel during the evening, when they would meet up with anyone who did not want to go back to a lonely bedroom. They simply threw caution to the wind and lived for the day.

On Friday nights, after being paid, Jean and Margaret would go to the off-licence and buy lots of drinks, like Vodka, Bacardi and Whisky, then they'd go partying all night. Most Saturday mornings they would get sacked, for either still being hung over, or late for work.

Margaret would then call out, "Right everyone out!"

They would leave all the tables to be cleared and cleaned. As the manager could not get any more staff to work for him, he used to come to them cap in hand and reinstate them all.

After a heavy night on the town, the girls would put on their overalls ready for the manager's wake-up call in the morning, so that they would be ready for work. This happened a few times, and in the end he gave up sacking them.

Sandown was a favourite for the hippie community, and the café also became a favourite haunt of theirs. The girls became good friends with the hippies. When they came in for chips and gravy, Margaret and Jean would put either eggs under their chips or a sausage, or anything else they could hide so that they could get a cheap meal. The downside of becoming friends with the hippies were nits. They used to have to check each other's hair on a regular basis!

The girls came back to Burnley for the winter season, with a view of trying a different resort in the coming summer months. They joined the unemployment statistics, with the prospect of finding a menial job to ensure that they remained solvent. Money was essential, not so much important, but they needed enough to pay board at home, and to maintain their social life in a manner to which they had become accustomed. It always seemed to be Kath that the clerk at the Employment Office found work for. She even had an interview at the famous M & S store, but she made it quite clear to them that she had no intention of working in a shop. It was eventually sorted out, and Kath and Margaret went to work in a factory in Todmorden, which is about twelve miles from Burnley. They travelled with other workers in a mini-van, which picked them up at Burnley Bus Station. Jean however, leant towards office work, and found a temporary job at the Great Universal Store in Burnley, which was concerned with catalogue sales.

In August 1972, as well as toiling for two weddings, Audrey and Philip gained independence from the rent office at Burnley Borough Council, by becoming eligible for a mortgage, and owning their own property. They purchased a humble three-bedroomed terraced house, number 47 Westmorland Street, just two rows from Paisley Street. As fate had it, Westmorland Street had been the destiny of Mr. Manning and his daughter Kath. They had moved from Little Cornwall to number 38, a few years after the Trickett's.

Margaret kept in close contact with Mr. and Mrs. Trickett, enjoying the varicoloured company of their family. By now they had a relatively new edition, their sixth child, Janine Bernadette, who was born in 1969, just as dusk muted the copper tones of autumn. Janine was a beautiful child with soulful almond eyes, and was their big surprise.

During the winter months, and in between their seasonal work, Kath and Margaret always returned to work at Mons Mill in Todmorden where Christine had also worked since Justin was ten months old. She had been convinced by Margaret and Kath that it was a great place to work.

Whilst Christine had been on maternity leave, the girls used to take a day off work every month and spend it with Christine and her young baby. They hinted that the company did not mind them playing truant, and so she was persuaded to work there, telling herself that she too could have a day off if it got too much for her. Although, the work was extremely exhausting, and not at all like the clean, pleasant atmosphere that she had known at Mullards, there was a lot of laughter and camaraderie. Christine met a life-long friend called Gwen, who looked after her on her very first day.

In order to remain employed by the end of the training week, Christine needed to master the art of breaking the coloured sticky tape, which would entwine the array of wires that stretched out to terminals of different lengths. She struggled relentlessly. Gwen came to her rescue by showing Christine the knack of pulling the tape just far enough for it to stretch and become thinner, thus easier to snap off the roll.

In 1972, Margaret and Kath returned home and began working at Mons Mill once more where they became friendly with Sandra, a girl from Rochdale. They told her about their experiences working in hotels, and Sandra became extremely keen to join them on their next adventure.

Soon it was the end of March 1973, bringing with it the time for them to get back to life in the fast lane. Jean, Margaret and Sandra chose Bournemouth for their seasonal work.

However Kath's dad had become unwell, and she felt unable to leave him, so she waved the three girls off, and carried on with her work at Mons Mill.

The families had become a safety net for each other. Mr. and Mrs. Hand and Margaret and Jean's regular letters and telephone calls were Kath's deliverance when her dad was taken into hospital. It was a nerve-racking saga for father and daughter, that started when John asked Kath to make him an appointment at the doctors. This in itself worried Kath because he had always benefited from good health.

The day John saw the doctor he was ordered to go home, put his feet up and do nothing. A cardiac specialist would make a domiciliary visit later that evening. John and his children sat in shock as the Consultant explained he needed a pacemaker fitting as soon as possible.

Kath cried inconsolably, her dad had never been in hospital before, and she had never really lived alone. She was only twenty-three years old, but suddenly felt fifty as her world was collapsing around her. She felt battered and without any armour for protection.

"You'll be in Blackpool Victoria Hospital for four weeks," assured the doctor. "They're pioneers in heart surgery you know, so you'll have the best care."

Within days arrangements had been made. Kath bought John new pyjamas and a dressing gown, but when the ambulance arrived and the driver told him Kath wasn't allowed to travel with them, and that she would have to follow on the bus, he refused to go.

"Mr, Manning, please don't waste our time and yours," cautioned the ambulance man. "We are only doing our job, and as I see it you've got no choice in the matter."

Kath pleaded with her dad to let the men wheel him into the vehicle.

After much persuasion he reluctantly agreed. As he kissed a tearful Kathleen, he shouted, "I won't be staying so there's no point in me taking that bag."

Kath made her way to Burnley Bus Station where she boarded the Blackpool-bound bus. Much to the embarrassment of other passengers she cried shamelessly as the bus sifted through towns and villages, weaving its way alongside pastures to the far side of Blackpool.

At the hospital, Kath felt so unfamiliar with her surroundings that her mind was totally disorientated. Her eyes were red and swollen with all the crying, and her head throbbed. The nurses seemed to stampede along the corridors with the urgency of their work.

Eventually Kath found John slumped in a chair. He appeared pale and no longer straight-backed, really looking his age. What upset her most was seeing him in someone else's pyjamas and an old dressing gown that had turned pink in the wash!

She didn't go straight home to Westmorland Street, but instead went to Mrs. Hand's.

"Hey love," said a comforting Mrs. Hand. "I wouldn't like to think a child of mine was going home every night to a cold empty house, and you're not either. Let me go round with ya for ya night-clothes and things, and ya can stay here as long as ya need to."

John Manning felt so much happier knowing Kathleen, (he would not recognise the name Kath) was being well cared for. He agreed to stay, and was even pleased to wear his first pair of pyjamas and new matching dressing-gown.

Jean met Barrie, her husband to be, during this time in Bournemouth. Ironically, it was whilst drunk and hitch-hiking a lift home to the hotel where they were working. Richard, who later married Sandra, the girl from Rochdale, stopped to take the girls home.

Richard drove round and round as he and Barrie were still trying to pluck up enough courage to ask the girls out. If Jean and Sandra had not been quite so merry they would have realised that they were being stalled, for they could have walked home far quicker. Eventually though Richard and Barrie arranged to meet up with the girls again. And so it seemed that the seasonal work in Bournemouth enriched the lives of the girls who had now met their partners and did not intend to return to Burnley. Margaret did return however, to the joy of her parents.

The time when the girls worked away was a very sad time for Mrs. Hand, because not only did she lose Margaret, but she missed the other girls. Christine, Carole and Kath visited, but it was not the same without Margaret, and without spending all the evening talking and chatting about the events in their lives. They weren't there to get ready to go out, nor were they there in the morning when Mrs. Hand peeped in Margaret's bedroom to see how many cups of tea would be needed before breakfast.

Margaret had met her husband to be Michael, during the summer of 1973. It was a summer of madness, but fun. She was working as a chambermaid in the Angus Hotel in the affluent part of Bournemouth with Jean. Michael was unlike any of the boys she had met before, like a distinct mammal. It was his power to be different that attracted her to him, rather than his long, lean frame or his fast sporty car. He dared to wear a sandy-coloured beard, and beads around his neck, and he played with a band from gig to gig.

There was just one obstacle, his mother. Although at this stage she was unable to halt the progression of this relationship. Michael was well-bred and lived in splendour with his widowed mother in Lymington, not far from the New Forest. Her detached bungalow was very upmarket, but for all her wealth she was bitter and twisted.

The North/South divide was prominent in her judgement of Margaret. How could Michael ever have associated, yet alone fallen in love and want to marry, a girl from a working-class background? The very thought sent piercing pains right through her head like firecrackers jumping and sparking. But Michael did not give in to her scenes of disapproval. They married in March, 1974, like her friends, in St. Mary Magdalene's. Michael, like Jean, wasn't a Roman Catholic.

Mr. Hand always gave a little advice, "Stick with your own kind." He would sometimes ask if a new boy came along, "Is he a left footer?" meaning is he Catholic? But for the friends that weren't of the faith, he made no criticism.

Despite Michael's lack of faith he was willing to respect Margaret's choice and he treated him equally.

All went well at the wedding, with friends for bridesmaids, and friends' parents for wedding guests. Margaret's new mother-in-law was guest of honour at Mrs. Hand's house, for the preparation and post period of the wedding. Margaret, Michael and his mother all travelled back to the South together. Mrs. King Senior totally ignored Margaret's parents during her stay, choosing to reject their goodness and hospitality by staying in her upstairs room.

As the newly-weds bid farewell to Mr. and Mrs. Hand and Burnley, Mrs. Hand worried justifiably for her daughter. What sort of support could she hope to receive from a mother-in-law with such low scruples? How would Margaret ever tolerate such a beast of a woman?

They settled in a small flat in the fishing town of Lymington. It was cosy, yet sophisticated, and situated close to the harbour in the thick of culture. At the beginning of June, Margaret announced that she was pregnant, much to her mother-in-law's displeasure. Without discussion the couple's belongings were moved into the huge bungalow whilst Margaret was at work. This was a vain attempt to win her son back under her spell. She was like a junta seizing power, but she was on a fool's errand if she thought that she could capture Margaret. Michael had been at her beck and call for years, but his new wife was of a totally different make up. She was a woman's role model, standing up for her rights.

Carole and Alan spent Burnley Wake's fortnight on the Isle of Wight. It was only right and proper to meet up with Margaret and Michael who lived just across the Solent. The four of them, along with one-year old Keelie, spent the day seeing the sights of Bournemouth and the surrounding areas. Nothing was too much trouble for Michael; he was the chauffeur for the day. They called at the bungalow which was now Margaret's home. The nimble shrivelled woman dressed in black, wore her hair tied up in a bun at the nape of her neck, emphasising her stone-edged features. With grey narrow eyes, and the sallowest complexion, her pale thin lips and deep revealing lines, one could guess her origins to be North Mediterranean. Nevertheless she was a picture of misery, as though to exemplify gloom and wretchedness.

The first week in August Margaret and Michael came up to Burnley to visit her parents at Paisley Street, for two weeks. Mr. and Mrs. Hand had thought it wise to holiday for the first week touring Ireland, to allow the young married couple time and space together, a little privacy, a sort of second honeymoon. Afterwards they would indulge in spending time with their daughter and new son-in-law during the second week of their stay. Catching up with her old friends was also on Margaret's agenda. People were of a different breed up North to people in the South, for they were always friendly and warm. Although she often met up with Jean and Barrie, she missed the laughter and company of her friends, like a prisoner yearns for freedom.

They arrived after a long tedious journey on Friday evening. Mr. and Mrs. Hand had already left for their summer break. Late Sunday afternoon, Carole had a telephone call from Margaret.

"Hiya, Carole, it's me, Margaret, I wondered if I could come and stay at your house for a while. Michael doesn't feel well and needs to go home to the doctors."

She was welcomed into Carole and Alan's home with open arms, but they did not realise it was the beginning of the end of Margaret's marriage. Michael returned to Bournemouth with a sore throat and never returned to Burnley. Margaret was adamant she was not going South unless he telephoned her. Neither conversed, so that was the end without much trying, despite her being pregnant..

The girls decided to spend a weekend at Blackpool for some respite. Christine was taking Justin, Carole was taking Keelie, Margaret was pregnant with Ryan, and Kath was helping her sister Joan, with her two children Mark and Joanne. Unfortunately the day before, Carole was rushed into hospital with a miscarriage. Everyone felt a great sense of sadness, feeling in a state of helplessness as Carole lay in the hospital bed and told them all to still go to Blackpool as planned. They did, but it was not quite the same knowing that Carole was not there with them. It seemed that the friends would always be so, even whilst they now had their own families, their friendship grew deeper.

Ryan was born on the 13th January 1975 to a loving mother and admirable grandparents.

It had been in 1974 when the Trickett's broke with tradition by sending their youngest daughter, Janine to St. Augustine's Primary School in Lowerhouse Lane. Janine was happy in this caring establishment, which was renowned as Miss Hornby's Academy, just as it was when the Manning children attended. When Margaret, a single parent, came to enter her son Ryan into education, St. Augustine's was also her choice. Janine was only too happy to volunteer her services, enabling Margaret to carry on with her work at Mons Mill. Being six years his senior, Janine was capable of catching the bus to and from Lowerhouse with Ryan in her charge.

Even Janine laid claims to Mrs. Hand's warmth and generosity. She, like her elder brothers and sisters before her, had a morning paper round when she reached her teenage years. Philip insisted that she took Cindy, their pet dog with her. Cindy was a white wire-haired standard poodle, with protective instincts.

"Take her with ya," he'd say, "nobody will harm ya when she's with ya." Philip was also saving himself a morning walk.

Janine didn't mind, Cindy was as good as a loyal friend; in fact she made sport of being able to leave her tied to a gate whilst she ran up the path and posted the paper through the letter-box.

One week Cindy was in season, and one particular dog annoyed the pair of them by following and sniffing, even attempting to mount Cindy. Janine toyed with the idea of taking her home, but realised that she was next door to Mrs. Hand's house. Seeing a light coming from the hall she decided to knock. It was still dark, being only quarter to seven, with no one around apart from the offending dog.

Mrs. Hand answered the door in her quilted dressing gown, with a few rollers in her hair, fixed with a fine mesh hairnet, "What is it love?" she asked Janine, a little worriedly.

"Mrs. Hand, I hope you don't mind, but Cindy's in season, and there's a dog at the gate that won't leave us alone. Can I leave her here whilst I finish my papers?"

"Hey, course ya can love, give her me here. You get them papers posted and collect her on the way back."

"Thanks Mrs. Hand," said a very grateful Janine, "I won't be long."

Mrs. Hand had Cindy by the lead as Leonard made his way to the bathroom downstairs.

"Hey, lass," he said to his wife, "have we taken to dog sitting now? They all know where to come, don't they?" he chuckled.

Chapter Sixteen

During the in between years the friends gathered for all kinds of good reasons. There were weddings, christenings, birthdays, and thankfully very rarely, funerals. There was always lots of chin wagging and gossip regarding who's marrying who, who's divorcing who and who's expecting babies. During these passing times, trust had been built like a round enclosed theatre without gaps, but filled with plenty of support. Some of the friends suffered personal tragedies. Margaret was the strongest pillar at such times, liberally pouring out her strength and offering hope. She was honest, even when it stung like a red hot poker, but if she had something to say, then she would always say it.

One of the many recollections of good times over the years was when the friends took their 'cradle Catholics' to see Pope John Paul II in Heaton Park, Manchester. The old St. Mary Magdalene's Church and School, that had stood for almost a century, had been demolished to make way for the essential motorway – the M65. Two modern structures had been built, one in Gawthorpe Road, and one on the edge of the motorway.

Here parishioners met at 11:00 p.m. to join the convoy of double-decker buses taking the holy pilgrims to Heaton Park. Over a million people, a mixture of young and old, met for the memorable occasion, with sleeping bags and blankets in tow. Flasks of hot drinks and sandwiches to fill hungry tummies, were part of the belongings which were taken. Children took snatches of sleep, packed in tightly alongside their parents, snuggled like sardines in a sealed can. With nightfall came the chill, but the warmth of excitement aired their bones. The dew on the grass had soaked the quilted sleeping bags, but who cared?

A mass exodus were waiting patiently to greet the Papal hero. The drizzle began whilst everyone waited for the Popemobile to arrive, causing enthusiasm to cool slightly. An hour or so later the sun burst its banks as Pope John Paul II suddenly appeared. A canopy of yellow flags and patriotic banners were stretched and waved. Loud cheery sirens echoed for a mile and beyond. The crowd was exhilarated, some folk were overcome with emotional exaltation, whilst others raised their voices in the harmonious song, which had been practised over previous months with much piety. New and legendary hymns rang out across the heavens. Some cast inhibitions, and spoke in tones of how the people in parables must have felt as Jesus preached to them, as hearts and souls were touched.

Margaret took her only son Ryan. Christine now had two sons, Justin and Alex, and Carole's children Keelie and Dominic were all part of the entourage. Their ages ranged from five to eleven years. Christine and Carole had both left baby daughters at home, Lucy and Melissa, with their daddies watching the scene on the television. Holy Mass was celebrated with much honour, whilst combining the Sacrament of Holy Orders for ten young men who had trained for the priesthood from the diocese. With declarations of their love for God and His Church stated aloud in front of the crowd. The families of these newly ordained priests, must have been uplifted by such nobility.

The service ended; the Pope bid farewell to his people, and left by helicopter. As the vehicle hovered over the mass crowds, the sky was suddenly blackened with storm clouds.

Ideas of phenomena spread as the children exclaimed, "Miracle, it must be a miracle!"

As the heavens opened, true enough the sun had lavished its rays across Manchester during the Pope's divine presence. This became the talking point, whilst the vast numbers left for home. For many people Manchester's largest public garden, was now consecrated grounds. The so called 'miracle' was the topic of conversation for weeks afterwards, convincing the folks who were not able for one reason or another to make the journey, that God's presence had been shown just like the supernatural events of two thousand years ago, like at The Wedding Feast of Cana, or Christ walking on the water.

Mr. Hand, now in the eventide of his life, was particularly thrilled to think that his small grandson had witnessed such a spectacular event.

Kath spent Saturday afternoon's with Margaret and Ryan going into town. Forever the boss, Margaret would nudge Kath as the bus would show itself at the tip of the brew, and tell Kath to run and make sure that the driver waited for her and Ryan. Although Margaret often dealt out her orders, they were always carried out, because they were *always* issued with a smile.

One such Saturday Ryan had gone to a party, so the two girls found themselves with the opportunity to go for a lunch-time drink in the Broadsword Pub which stood defiantly at the corner of the market square. Kath's future husband Michael (known to most as Mick) was merrily drunk, having been celebrating with his friend. Silliness oozed from them; they were pretending to have a dog with them. This ploy worked, for it had attracted the attention of Kath and Margaret.

Michael walked up to Kath and cheekily stated as he staggered through the doors, "I'm going to marry you!"

Kath smiled to herself, "Yes," she thought, "that would be nice."

Several weeks later, without Ryan, the girls ventured into the Broadsword more aware this time that they might catch sight of Michael and his friend.

They did.

Michael asked Kath, "Will you let me take you out?"

"No," she answered, because she was seeing an Italian in the hope of a visit to Italy, though the trip never materialised as Kath never saw him again.

Christine and Kath had gone for a quiet drink in the Clarion Club one Thursday night when in walked Michael. Kath pointed him out to Christine, who declared that she knew him vaguely as he lived on the

Stoops Estate where she lived, and his brother had been in Carole's class at St. Mary Mag's School.

He came over and invited Kath out again, but Kath was playing hard to get, and told him that she would think about it.

When Kath had gone to the toilets, Michael asked Christine to work on her. Christine said that she would do just that.

So it was that Kath and Michael were married in 1981, just two years before Margaret married her beloved Colin.

Margaret had had her eye on Colin before they had been introduced, though she had not mentioned this to anyone, as Margaret decided when, and with whom she would share her thoughts. He had been in the Clarion Club where Margaret, Kath and Christine occasionally went on a Thursday night. Had she said something then, well Christine could have enlightened her, as she recognised him as Arthur's brother from nearby Harold Avenue. Walking home from Mass one Sunday morning Colin passed Margaret and Kath, he nodded and half smiled at them as he entered the Havelock Pub.

"Who's that?" Margaret asked Kath.

"Oh, he's a friend of Michael's, he's called Colin Fort, he's on his own too!" exclaimed Kath, at the same time watching Margaret's facial expression closely.

But she gave nothing away as usual.

The autumn leaves fell, and winter quickly approached; the festive season had arrived. Christmas time was for the children, whilst the New Year's activities were for the grown-ups. Plans were being discussed on how to welcome in the year of 1980?

In the midst of things Margaret told Kath that she was not going out to celebrate, because everyone else had a partner to take with them. It did not bother her, for the last thing on her mind was a partner!

However Kath took matters into her own hands, she told Michael that she would meet him just before the magical hour of midnight, leaving the 70's in the past. Margaret was informed by her friend that she was going out to celebrate, therefore she was not given any choice in the matter. The evening turned into a real success, when Michael met them later that evening with Margaret's future husband, Colin.

Throngs of people had gathered in the tiny pub eagerly awaiting the chimes of Big Ben, which soon would be ringing from the television set above the packed bar. The atmosphere was hazy with smoke, the large decorations were gaudy and cheap, but that did not matter in this place because they were likely to be ripped down on the stroke of midnight. It was difficult to get through the crowd to where Michael stood with his friend, as everyone was so busy chatting and laughing that they did not take any notice of polite interruptions. It was up to Kath and Margaret to be a bit more forceful in making their way through the crowd.

Amidst all this, in true romantic style Margaret and Colin's eyes had made contact across the room, rendering them both completely unaware of all the banter and frivolity which was going on all around them. They gazed at one another and then chemistry began to do its job. It was soon evident that each had found their soul mate. The relationship blossomed and they soon became one.

After their wedding they settled down to family life, where Ryan gained a new brother and sister, and even more to his delight, found a special person who became his dad.

Seventeen Chapter

Jean was very much settled in Bournemouth, and was ever so delighted when both her children were born. Adam came first, then Claire. It was always an adventure to find Jean's house when the families of Christine and Peter, and Carole and Alan went down South for their summer holidays, but Margaret had very good reasons for staying clear of Bournemouth and its neighbouring towns. The families would land themselves on Jean's doorstep for the afternoon, and the girls would catch up on the latest news, whilst the men would go off to the pub for a pint.

This pleased Barrie, because he felt that all he ever heard from Jean, particularly in their early years together, was Burnley this and Burnley that. He had heard perhaps too many times about the capers that the girls got up to whilst growing up. Barrie had a lot to live up to with his name – Barrie White, as the famous Barry White was a great soul singer that the girls often danced to as they admired his deep husky voice.

When Jean and Barrie took their summer break they found themselves in Burnley, where they would stay with Jean's sister Maureen, and her husband David. Never once did Jean not meet her treasured friends; there was always something special arranged by the girls. Jean also always ensured that she visited 1, Paisley Street.

Mr. Hand died on his 80th birthday on July 2nd 1983, he was sitting in his favourite place, his beloved garden. Constantly he had been seen with his tools in his hand; always he was pottering between the shed and the garden. He enjoyed his pint-pot of tea and the sandwich that Mrs. Hand made every day for lunch, where he would just sit relaxing on the bench which he had made himself many years previously.

It was here that Kath and Michael found him that Saturday afternoon, having walked through the enchanted garden, passing the honey-bees and red admirals busy about their work. They had gone to wish him *'Happy Birthday'*, but it was never said. He just looked asleep, his face was so peaceful, but he wasn't. He had died of a heart attack, as instantly as he would have taken his next breath. He wore his well-worn brown smock, which was his trademark; in his hand was his hammer, as though he had been pondering which job to undertake next. It was up to Kath to find Margaret and Mrs. Hand and tell them the sad news. She did not relish this task, but knew that it would be easier coming from her, and perhaps somewhat more comforting for Margaret to know that it was someone she loved who had found her dad.

Kath was able to empathise with Margaret, because it was exactly one year earlier that Margaret had to tell

Kath about *her* dad. It was Joan, Kath's sister, who contacted Margaret when she called at Paisley Street to use the telephone. Joan had taken her children to visit their Granddad, and much to their distress found that he had died in his sleep. Joan had asked Margaret to break the news to Kath. Now Kath felt somewhat privileged that she could return the task which Margaret had once done for her. It increased their closeness, both knowing how hard it was to lose their fathers.

Chapter Eighteen

Margaret was designed for married life, she and Colin worked hard, getting to know each other's ways, little quirks, expressions, annoying little habits, dislikes and pleasures. Fitting in with his children Nick and Shelby, was a task which Margaret knew she would achieve. The children, all similar ages, gelled together in the need for some love and stability, which they got from inside 1, Richmond Street.

To pay for all the luxuries which Margaret wanted for her family, she began working on the nearby Coal Clough Lane, at Kathleen Lord's established florist and greengrocers. This part-time work enabled her to be at home both before the children went to school, and when they arrived home.

Kathleen's shop was stretched over two buildings, one holding the flowers and all the paraphernalia required to transform single stems into wondrous bouquets, rich with colour, as silver and gold strands entwined amongst the greenery, blending in perfectly with the green and white Gypsophila. Works of art were created by Catherine, Bev and the other girls, over the time span when Margaret worked alongside them, albeit next door. Here she stacked bags of potatoes, weighed out broth mix in winter, for it was always a good-seller during the biting cold weather, and guaranteed to warm you through and through, as Margaret would endorse this to the customer.

Apples, some shiny red, others limey green, or even a mixture of the two, would be displayed so very neatly, that the customer hardly dared to pick any up for fear of sending them all tumbling down. Tropical fruits could be seen, and Margaret always knew the unfamiliar names of them, and the country from which they had been imported.

Out in all weathers, Margaret and Kathleen could be seen wearing several layers, with a fleece on top to keep the cold out, and wearing fingerless gloves to help to keep their hands warmer, as they served their customers. Margaret wore her jester-type hat, with her hair dishevelled beneath it. A mustard skirt, royal blue tabard and black woolly socks and ankle boots completed Margaret's attire. Winter time was always a bugbear. The weather was never in their favour, often wet and wild, with the wind howling through the open-fronted section of the store. Cold, crisp days were just as mean, biting at fingers and toes, leaving painful chilblains behind which tormented the worker's hands and feet. There was no respite until springtime appeared. Christmas was always one of the busiest festive seasons, for the trade brought a miniature forest of Norwegian Spruce, which lined the whole pavement, leaving very little room for pedestrians and potential customers of the butchers, the bookmakers or the barbers, which were situated alongside Kathleen's business on Coal Clough Lane.

Margaret complained avidly every winter, but she loved the shop, and shared the gossip, good news and bad news. Ears pricking up at every conversation, she had the art of listening to several conversations at once, even picking up evidence of people's affairs. She could deliver and absorb more information than the local newspaper. Margaret often gave advice on which potatoes were best for boiling, or which ones made the better chips, whilst tactically rooting for the latest gossip. Her persona changed minute by minute, and Margaret's voice was on a roller coaster. It went up and down an octave, according to the status of the customer. The people who really knew her found this very amusing.

Christine was in the shop selecting fruit; Margaret was in deep conversation with Amelia, the bank-manager's wife.

"Yes Amelia, these potatoes are excellent for roasting, you have made the right choice, I use them all the time," Margaret spoke in her feigned upper-class tone.

Whilst handling the oranges, Christine had to bite her lip as she chuckled at the conversation she had just witnessed, thinking to herself "Here she goes again with the amateur dramatics."

Amelia left the shop, delighted with the service, and Christine got to the till and mimicked Margaret's voice, "Would they be the same potatoes that I bought last week that turned to mush when I roasted them?"

Margaret replied in her Burnley twang, "Don't be stupid Christine, you didn't cook 'em right!"

Rita, who was senior to both Margaret and Kathleen, had become a firm friend, and was often in the shop just camping, or idling the time away, interrupted their conversation in her deep gruff voice, "Margaret, is that why mine went to mush as well?"

"Oh shut up, you're as bad as her."

The three of them laughed heartily, as Margaret stated that she was only 'keeping up appearances'.

Life in the shop was for most of the time a bundle of laughs, bringing amusement to customers, delivery men and the rest of the staff. This compensated them all well as it brought warmth and smiles on cold winter days. There were many amusing incidents, but one which will be recalled over and over again providing tears of laughter, was the first and only time that Margaret volunteered to deliver a Christmas Tree. It was all because Amelia wanted the grandest tree, the largest that Kathleen had left, which was over seven feet high.

Frank, Amelia's husband came to buy their Christmas tree, "Only the best will do, you know what her ladyship is like. I've been told to come home with nothing less than a seven foot one," moaned Frank.

"Does she know that the average ceiling is only seven foot six?" laughed Kathleen. "We've a grand one out here," she continued, "but how on earth are you gonna get it home?"

"Ah, that's a point," he said studying, hand on his hip and scratching his chin.

For reasons known only to herself Margaret volunteered her services. "I'll help you, Frank," she offered in her genteel voice reserved for professionals.

"Wait a minute, Margaret," Kathleen jumped in. "How are you gonna manage that?"

"Easy if we get cracking," Margaret answered. "Come on Frank, you take the top and I'll take the bottom. One, two, three, lift."

They both heaved, and then slowly walked in unison upwards towards the posh houses of Pasturegate.

Kathleen turned to her observing customers bewildered, yet laughing saying, "I'll be really worried until she gets back, it's a blooming long way to carry a Norwegian Spruce!"

Margaret glimpsed in front of her, whilst questioning her own intelligence. "What on earth have I gotten myself into?" She bristled at the thought.

There was no one to respond to her moans. Frank was six feet in front, but with the howling wind and the thickening snow flurries that had threatened all day now falling, she somehow felt alone. Wondering who might see and recognise her, she kept her brown suspicious eyes hidden beneath her multi-coloured jester hat.

"Heaven knows what folk would think?" she muttered to herself.

Her red and green checked three quarter length coat, gave her the traditional look of a lumber-jack, and although she was shod in her lace-up boots, which were good strong footwear for the weather, her feet ached, yet she felt she was lifting lead with each step, they were so numb at having been penetrated by the cold all day. She began to limp.

On reaching Amelia's pre-war detached home, with regret she moaned, "I feel as though I've just felled this bloody tree meself, I think I could do with the bus fare home if you don't mind." She had slipped up, her voice was back to the one used for commoners, the ordinary folk without airs or graces.

Frank laughed out loud, whilst his wife struggled with what to say but, "Thank you."

"Come on Margaret, step into the Celica and I will drive you back to work," Frank offered gracefully.

Kathleen was waiting, "Hey, Margaret, are you all right? Michael would have taken the tree up in the van, I didn't expect you to take it." Her boss showed genuine concern for Margaret, reflecting anxiety as she spoke.

"Yeh, well I'll not be doing it ever again, it nearly put me blinking lights out!" Margaret's voice was full of comical sarcasm.

Tom Metcalfe could not wait to go and purchase his fruit and vegetables the following morning from Kathleen's. But nine o'clock was too early. Margaret would be crammed, and the last thing he wanted was to annoy her. Yet he enjoyed an audience. "No eleven o'clock would be better," he told himself. There would be more shoppers around, in fact Friday was the busiest day! Some of the regulars would appreciate a funny tale, and Margaret would have mellowed after her mid-morning coffee. In he strolled at eleven o'clock precisely. His timing could not have been better.

Rita, a jovial character who loved the company of the staff and customers alike was sat on a stool, feet dangling, whilst her hands cupped the beaker of steaming coffee for warmth. Rita absorbed every word uttered in the shop, living alone since her husband David, had past away. It gave her something to ponder over, a pastime to ease the long lonely days. She could often be seen helping Margaret cut up the vegetables to make up the broth mix.

Tom rubbed his gloved hands together. "Morning ladies, by it's a bitter one this morning."

"Morning Tom," everyone chorused.

The shop was just as busy as he had hoped.

"Can I help you Tom?" asked Kathleen, ever so obligingly.

"Oh, yes please, Kathleen, I'd like to buy one of those lovely Christmas trees you have outside. I want a big one, mind. Oh, and I'd like that new delivery service you've got. What do you say Margaret?" glancing over to where she was weighing fruit. "By the way I'm glad to see you are home safe and well dear," he grinned.

Margaret looked up faking confusion. "What ya on about, Tom, I don't know what ya mean," she spoke sheepishly.

"Don't tell me it wasn't you carrying that monster of a tree up the lane yesterday. I was stood at our bay window waiting of the grandchild coming by, when Frank passed shouldering the top half of this bloody big thing. Ten minutes later Margaret appears struggling with the stump end. Well I thought, I've seen it all," I shouted to Phyllis, "I think that they've stolen that bloody thing from Trafalgar Square!"

The place was in uproar as customers visualised Frank and Margaret with what must have seemed as though they were walking miles apart.

Margaret added fuel to the laughter when she commented, "You can forget that new delivery service. It's the first and last time I deliver fruit and vegetables, never mind a flaming Christmas Tree!"

For days people pulled Margaret's leg, but she took it all in good spirits, laughing along with everyone else for she was never one to be phased by a funny story.

Chapter Nineteen

The friends, together with their partners, shared Margaret and Colin's good company in one form or another. Holidays and weekend breaks became regular annual events. To break away from the dark wet days of November, Paula and Keith, mutual friends to all, rallied round and brought people together to share a weekend of fun in the Vegas of the North – Blackpool! Amidst the glittering neon flashing lights, candy floss, toffee apples, the smell of fresh fish and chips, hot dogs, kiss-me-quick hats and the wurlitzing sounds of the fairground music, the couples let their hair down, whilst they left the now teenage children at home fending for themselves.

They stayed at the famous Queen's Hotel on the Queen's Promenade. Its furniture and décor had seen better days, for once it had been splendid, and although it still boasted an air of class, it needed to be updated.

It was whilst staying there that they sneaked into the neighbouring hotel, which boasted of *'The best cabaret in Blackpool'*. Long after the show and the disco had finished, and the last of the guests had retired to their beds, the friends lingered at their table singing their own rendition of the ballads of the *Drifters, 'Saturday night at the Movies* and *'Under the Boardwalk'*, much to the dismay of the bouncer, who wanted to retire himself.

All in good fun he said, "I'm glad you lot are not staying here, or I'd never get to bed!"

Laughter reigned as the couples realised that they were not very successful with their antics of sneaking in. From then on they all stayed at this hotel on future visits to Blackpool, and became well-known and subsequently good friends with the staff, who appeared to be there year after year.

Margaret, Colin, Christine, Peter, Carole and Alan had booked to go on holiday for a week to Turkey, for what was to be time in the sun and sea, and an interesting dose of culture, and plenty of booze! Sadly Margaret and Colin had to cancel, owing to Mrs. Hand being admitted to hospital. The sadness felt about losing their company was short-lived.

Margaret turned it around to laughter when she announced, "Well I'm glad we're not going really, because the lads would only get shot in the back of the head, but we would be dragged up into the mountains and raped."

The thought of the not so young, not so slim, and not so fit middle-aged females being dragged into the mountains by young Turks, caused such amusement and jokes for a long time to come.

She even laughed herself the following year when finally they were all able to holiday together in Turkey. Whilst marching down the steep hillside of Hisaruno towards Olu deniz, Margaret glanced up at the steep gullies of the grey mountainside which were the backcloth of the beautiful countryside. Reaching a height of over six thousand feet, these were the Babadag Mountain Range, and recalling her statement made the previous year, she turned to Christine and said laughingly, "Eeh Christine, they'd need a dammed big crane to get me and thee up there!"

Carole replied, "I think it's wishful thinking, that you'd be so lucky."

Colin replied, "It could be Alan and Peter they'd want!"

The fun and laughter made the long drag down less strenuous on the knees, and much more amusing. The day was to be spent in the company of friends, Margaret and Mick Scanlon, who were staying in a hotel overlooking the famous Blue Lagoon. Funny how a little political unrest can be so entertaining. There was no evidence of this, as they were shown nothing but genuine hospitality and respect, which ensured that the friends returned to holiday there on a couple more visits in the years that followed.

Chapter Twenty

The distance of time is a funny old thing, is it not? How many of us can fathom or understand it? Old Father Time, like the tidal waters, eludes no one, galloping on with the grace of a gazelle, without notice. Suddenly half a century is transformed into memories, with interesting snippets of our yesteryears.

This is how the girls felt, though they were girls no longer, but middle-aged women, old enough to be grandmothers. Indeed, Margaret's step-daughter, Shelby, had bore her and Colin two beautiful granddaughters, and a third one had just been announced. They were all steering towards their 50th birthdays when Jean visited Burnley in August 2000. A rare opportunity arose for them all to gather for an evening, just like the good old days. Margaret had not a problem with work, but both Kath and Christine worked at the hospital, with its rotating shift patterns, and therefore needed notice in order to request an evening off.

Christine, always determined by nature, won her goal with a little divergence. Through sheer hard work and a litany of courses, she became a High Dependency Sister on the Paediatric Unit at Burnley General Hospital. Indulging herself in the nursing profession, she excelled even her own high expectations. She regarded her work of caring for very sick children with the upmost importance and devotion. The children always came first and foremost. She glowed with warmth, like a talented harpist embracing her treasured musical instrument.

Kath, much to her own personal regret, did not complete her nurse training. She was now working as a nursing assistant on the busy Orthopaedic Wards at the same busy hospital as Christine. Kath applied herself well, but often looked back in repentance at quitting as a young cadet nurse. Being childless she enjoyed the shifts, spreading her time between Nellie, her elderly neighbour, Bonny – Kath and Mick's West Highland White – 'their baby', and of course sharing her company with Mrs. Hand.

Carole worked alongside her sister and other professionals, carrying out the work she felt she did the best, which was offering support to parents and relatives of children in hospital. Here her domesticated nature helped her fulfil the role; it was as though she had found her vocation.

Although the girls had all seen Jean individually during her visits to Burnley over the years, rarely did they manage an evening where they could all be together, for there was always one missing for one reason or another. Margaret had arranged that they meet at Christine's spacious home. She lived in a mid-terraced, garden-fronted house in Scott Park Road, where all boasted bay windows, and most were decorated with luxury drapes and artistic pelmets. The time to meet was Wednesday at 8:00 p.m. which seemed most suitable for everyone.

Carole reversed her car sneekily into Christine's neighbours' allocated spot, hoping they would not notice.

Kath, whom she had picked up along the way remarked, "Doesn't that sky look romantic?"

It had a mottling of crimson and light slate, as the sun made her low descent for the day. Carole glimpsed upwards without reply. Since 1992, the late summer evenings and early dawns she felt were marred with sadness, a confidence which she had shared with Christine. If you can imagine the beautiful sky and a vivid vapour trail, as a trail of sorrow dumped by a zealous jet plane, or a repetitious outpouring of grief – a sort of constant reminder.

Mrs. Trickett, their mother, had suffered from chronic depression and chest problems for decades. Emphysema ruled her world during the latter years of her life, but she was a creaking gate. They thought she would live forever. Out of the blue she was taken ill and admitted to hospital, where Philip her husband, and her six children kept a constant vigil over the weekend. She met her final retreat just as the fifth hour struck on Sunday, 30th August 1992. She died aged just fifty-nine years, leaving her family in shock and surrounded with devastation, for a twinkling light had faded from their starlit skies.

Carole and Kath made their way down the hall to Christine's bright homely kitchen, handing over a pack of lagers and a pack of Guinness. Jean had already arrived with Margaret, and she was in complete awe at the size of the whole house. She and Barrie lived in a bungalow in Wallisdown, Bournemouth with their two children, Claire and Adam. Although they had a lovely garden, their place was nothing like the size of this, and it had cost them the earth. They subsidised their income over the years by taking in French students. Giving them a warm bed and manufacturing packed lunches and evening meals, were really all that was required, not that it wasn't hard work, for at times it was.

Jean was now the secretary to the manager of a small local firm, a mile up the road from her house, towards Poole. Coincidentally, her boss David, was originally from Accrington, Lancashire just five miles or so from Burnley. Now and again, without realising it, David's voice would unwittingly reveal his Accrington accent, plunging Jean back to the memories of 'Accy Con Club', and of course you've guessed, Kevin McKoffery!

Everyone made themselves comfortable in Christine's tastefully decorated living-room, whilst husbands took a pint in the local pub, The Coal Clough. Jean looked up at the high ceiling, then to the marble fireplace on which sat expensive collectibles, giving the room an air of Victorian nostalgia.

After just one Bacardi and coke, (she only ever had one nowadays due to middle age migraines), Jean began laughing hysterically, almost unable to speak. "Oh, Christine, I was just thinking, here we are sat on Scott Park Road. Do you remember when you and Frances stood posing on top of the monuments in the park wearing your best dresses, revealing twelve inches of thigh?"

Margaret burst out laughing almost choking. "Never mind their best dresses they wore their hippie gear, beads everywhere, flowers in their hair, Indian headbands and everything. What on earth did they look like?"

Carole giggled, "I've got photographs to prove it. Look at us now. Greying hair hidden by colours from bottles, thickening waists, and just look at our sensible shoes, who would have believed it!"

Jean carried on in the same vein, "Yes, but Christine you and Frances sent your pictures to the Daily Mirror, hoping to feature as their Spring Birds."

"Yeh and me dad went barmy, do you remember?" asked Carole.

"Well," Margaret chirped. "She'd do anything to claim fame!"

This was all said as if Christine was not there, but she took it all in good humour and laughed just as much with them all. Time and age had crept up on them, a bit like someone creeping from behind and shouting 'boo'. Only Kath had kept her tall willowy figure. Margaret had always struggled with her weight, as had Christine since the birth of Justin over twenty-eight years ago. Even Carole, who Jean had once nicknamed 'Twiggy' because of her skinny frame, was beginning to look box-shaped.

They laughed about good times, sighed and talked of the sad events they had encountered over the years. Their memories were like a collection of valuable antiques locked away in Granny's attic, to be dipped into at leisure, whenever they met. They could easily have been in a time warp, travelling in reverse, back over thirty years. They could of course have been in 1, Paisley Street on 'confession night'.

Before the evening drew to an end, it was pointed out, as if Jean needed reminding, that Jean would be the first one of them to reach her half century. Carole felt they ought to start celebrating, just as they had done with 21st birthday parties, all those years before.

"I'll tell you what Jean," Carole suggested. "For your birthday the four of us will come down to you, and we'll have a girlie weekend. The children are all more or less grown up, there's nothing to stop us."

Everyone agreed to this suggestion before they said their goodbyes and made their way home. Although a fair bit of alcohol had been consumed, which left Jean feeling it was the drink talking, and not to take it all too seriously.

Jean, with Barrie and their two children travelled South to Wallisdown the third Sunday in August. The journey always seemed fraught with bumper to bumper motorway traffic and steaming weather. On Monday morning they would all resume their mandatory chores, whether it be work or school. She dwelt on the week she had left behind. It was good to catch up with her old friend Anne also, who Jean thought looked stunningly perfect.

Jean had stayed with her sister Maureen whose children had all now grown up. In fact Maureen had spoken proudly about her twelve-year old grand-daughter, updating Jean on all the latest news.

One of Jean's first ports of call was to see Mrs. Hand who now resided in an old folk's bungalow, at 77, Harold Street, literally two minutes walk from her old home on Paisley Street.

In deep thought she spoke aloud in her adopted Southern dialect. "Hard to believe isn't it Barrie how time slips through your fingers like tiny grains of sand."

Barrie being Barrie, just answered, "Yeh."

Jean always made the mistake of looking back on their trips back home. Now though she felt that she had something to look forward to, so roll on fifty!

Chapter Twenty-One

Autumn blended with winter as seasons seem to do these days, each slowly being deprived of their individual characteristic climate. Christmas festivities passed fulfilling wishes and expectations, pouring forth goodwill onto all, and drifting into resolutions for the coming year.

The girlie weekend get-together for Jean's birthday hadn't even been discussed since August. One thing the girls were slowly but surely realising, was that in their middle age, they were only capable of mastering one thing at a time. This seemed to be all due to hormonal changes, though any excuse was good enough, but in this instance it was perfectly natural. During such a busy period, impending luxurious thoughts were easily dismissed. The trip had crept into Carole's subconscious from time to time, but had been put on the back burner until her mind had cooled from the winter solstice.

By early January, Jean's birthday had reached the front of the queue in Carole's priorities. It had propelled itself forward now, and demanded urgent attention. Off duty had to be taken into consideration, plus family arrangements. Margaret felt Bournemouth would definitely need a two-night stay, especially when taking into account the travelling time for them to reach Bournemouth, and weekend shifts would only allow for one night.

A compromise was met, so that they wouldn't need to travel that far. The girls would drive two thirds of the way, and Jean from the South, one third. Bath, a city of famous historical culture, was agreed upon as the meeting place. Jean had one slight hiccup though, having passed her driving test thirty-two years previously, she had *never* ventured to drive on the motorway. But Barrie came to her rescue as her knight of the road in shining armour. He volunteered to chauffeur her to Bath on Saturday morning, then return for her on Sunday afternoon; so who says romance is dead?

January is the month of the guardian dog of doors and beginnings, so how appropriate that the girls were on a teenage revival trip then. This was a trip not like in the late sixties, when they thumbed lifts, danced in the disco till the early hours of the morning, and flashed false eyelashes at good-looking boys. No, now they were all lovingly contented with their hubbies at home, thank you very much. They planned a trip that only lifelong friendships can bring, filled with fun and laughter that no amount of material or money can buy. *People who have true friendship are the luckiest people in the world.* You can open it up at any age, like reflecting on a scrapbook, or a collector's album. But once you have found it, it's yours to keep and treasure.

Being the driver, Carole collected her friends, Kath, Margaret and Christine from their homes at 7:00 a.m. on Saturday morning, January 20th 2001. The weather was kind, as it was dry, bright, crisp and promising; this in itself is a seldom occurrence in Burnley – a town buried deep in the Pennines. The streets were bare, apart from an elderly gentleman strolling with his Jack Russell. It was evident the way he sought the warmth of the sunshine through the stripped branches of the trees that lined Lockyer Avenue, that he felt it quite beneficial to be out and about at such an unearthly hour on a weekend morning.

It was so quiet, the girls were so filled up with mounting excitement, that they felt that they were breaking all the house rules of a school's summer camp, like meeting at the end of the dormitory when everyone else was asleep. As they ferried down the M6 the traffic built up with other weekend drivers, but the road remained hassle free. There was much chatter whilst travelling the one hundred and fifty miles, to catch up with this and that, which was no more than the local gossip really!

The girls had a plan; they'd arranged to meet up with their pal Jean around 1:00 p.m. Time was on their side, so there would be no need to hurry. Mobile phone numbers had been exchanged the night before between Carole and Jean. They are wonderfully useful things aren't they? Well when you know how to use them that is! Carole had been given a phone for Christmas and had only ever used it once. She did not know how to install numbers into the menu or anything like that.

Jean had booked the accommodation only before setting out for Bath that morning. She'd used the tourist information, and the plan was for her to ring Carole with the name and address of the place.

As they progressed South on the verge of the intoxicating beauty of the Cotswolds, they heard the sound of Carole's phone, 'ring, ring'.

"Oh, be quick Christine, answer it," panicked Carole.

Christine answered the phone with ease, as using highly technical equipment came as second nature to her. Nursing sick children certainly demanded an understanding of machinery, whilst to the others it was tantamount to handling a hand-grenade.

"Hello Jean," Christine spoke calmly and collectedly.

Kath and Margaret automatically leaned forward in their seats, as if they were going to miss something if they didn't.

"Hiya, it's me," Jean answered. "I'm at the..."

Then the line went dead.

"Oh damm!" exclaimed Christine, "She's gone."

"It's okay, I've got her number," said Carole.

Christine twigged at the buttons for the address book, "Where?" she demanded.

"Oh not in there, I can't use that, it's in the filofax, in my bag," Carole explained.

Christine found the book that was as big as a house brick. "I don't believe this," she said. "What on earth do you carry this thing around with you for, when you can easily have the numbers in your phone?"

She might as well have been speaking to herself, because Carole simply kept her eyes on the road.

Christine dialled Jean's number only to hear Adam answer. They had swapped phones, and Jean had forgotten to tell Carole. Adam eventually solved the problem by ringing his mum, who was then connected with the girls.

"Hiya, it's me again," Jean laughed. "I'm at the hotel. It's called 'Haute Combe', on Newbridge Road, but I haven't a clue how to direct you here, so I'm going to put you onto the lady behind the reception desk." Then lowering her tone considerably she said, "I think she's the owner."

Without realising it Christine raised her voice a pitch to speak to the proprietor, who held an abundance of knowledge of the provincial area. In her West Country accent she guided them along meandering roads, passing through villages with strange sounding names. Medieval dwellings stood in the company of a cluster of affluent, up-to-date properties, then soon they were out on the open road again, until they dropped down to meet the intriguing heritage of Roman Bath. They did rather well really, just needing a U-turn once they'd reached the city.

The 'Haute Combe Hotel' stood proud, boasting period character renascent of the area. Margaret, Kath, Christine and Carole met Jean at the small counter, where the landlady stood looking relieved that they had arrived safe and well. That wasn't the only reason, Jean had chattered to her since her arrival three quarters of an hour earlier, no doubt keeping her from her weekend chores.

She introduced herself as Eileen, and she looked as fresh as a daisy. Tall and slim of build, her face was lit by the sparkle of her bright eyes, which complemented good cheekbones and an enviable complexion for her age. She owned a wonderful disposition, not at all stuffy, just warm and friendly, oozing confidence in her line of business.

"Ah," she said in her Northern Somerset drawl, "I've put Jean, Kath and Carole, (she obviously knew all their names without introduction) upstairs in the family room, and Christine and Margaret in the converted garage, if that is all right? You can make as much noise as you like then!"

Christine and Margaret looked at each other in shock horror wondering what on earth Jean had been telling this lady? The others looked at one another and covered their mouths in laughter, giggling like a crowd of schoolgirls. They picked up their bags, making their way to the appropriate rooms, and arranged to meet in the 'garage' in twenty minutes.

The quiet ones gingerly found their way to the garage, which turned out to be a delightful den, featuring a living and sleeping area, with a combined kitchen and small bathroom. A picture window, with a flowery organza curtain and floral drapes gave seclusion to this hideaway. Jean, Kath and Carole were knocking on the door, so Margaret opened it, allowing the three entry, laughing and giggling as they crossed the threshold. Jean carried photographs and champagne. Kath and Carole had a present each for the birthday girl.

Margaret demanded, "What have you been saying to the people here, they must think we're noisy alcoholics or something."

Jean could barely talk as she was grinning from ear to ear. "I only said that you smoke, and you both enjoy a drink."

"There's nothing truer than that," added Kath.

"Anyway," Jean announced, "I've brought some champagne, so let's crack it open."

Well the cork plopped without a sound. The drink poured without fizz or sparkle, but even so everyone toasted Jean's 50th birthday, a little late celebration, as her actual birthday had been earlier in the week.

"Cheers, cheers," they all clinked glasses and took sips, but each one was spat out nearly choking.

"Blooming heck Jean," Carole screamed, "where on earth have you got this from, it's awful?"

Faces were pulled in disgust.

"One of the students bought it for me when they were leaving our house," Jean explained.

Margaret promptly raised her voice in laughter, "Well I don't think they liked you very much! It tastes as though they've wee'd in the bottle."

Everyone hurriedly discarded their champagne down the sink.

Jean opened her presents of candles, a photo-frame, money in a card to treat herself, and a compact disc of all the old soulful sounds from the Mecca days. Then the photographs came out and laughter bellowed off the walls. Christine, ever hopeful, posing in Scott Park. Carole, Margaret, Jean and Linda enjoying Spain in 1970, or so it seemed. Only Margaret had seen Linda since, and only very occasionally in the last thirty years. She didn't reside in Burnley any longer, but it was good to include her in the reminisces of past times. There weren't any of Kath, for she had always been very camera shy. They would have to try to alter that over the next couple of days.

At 2:30 p.m. it was decided they would make their way into the city, and perhaps stroll around the shops and tour the artful wonders Bath proudly offered her multicultural visitors. After gathering essential gloves, scarves, hats and umbrellas, (just in case) they met in the reception.

Eileen was very helpful once more, "There's a Park and Ride, just a few minutes from here, it's really convenient."

"Oh, thank you," came Margaret's posh reply.

Once outside, Carole looked at her little car tucked neatly in the secure parking area, "It's a shame to move the car," she said to the others. "And it's a glorious day, a bit cold but not that bad."

"Okay come on then, what are we doing?" Margaret said back to her usual voice.

"Let's walk," said Jean, "the exercise will do us good."

They turned right to the Park and Ride as Eileen had instructed, Christine and Margaret each wearing dark, long-flowing macs, that hid a multitude of sins. Margaret also took to sporting a sort of headband that covered her ears and head like a halo. It was made of mock leopard-skin, in milky and chocolate browns blended with honey beiges. Margaret still looked scrumptious in these rich colours. The thinner girls were wrapped up in warm woollies and curly sheepskins that acted as insulation. No more were they trend-setters, but gladly dressed for comfort.

They walked at a relatively slow pace towards the Park and Ride for ten minutes or so. Two or three buses passed them head on with their destination marked as the City Centre.

"How many more of these buses are going to pass us?" Margaret raised her voice in annoyance.

Carole stopped on the spot, "Hang on a minute, we've walked for ten blooming minutes down here, and the buses are going in the opposite direction! We don't even need to go to the Park and Ride at all, the car is in the car park!"

This observation caused the five of them to howl in hysterics. They laughed until they cried, doubled up, then cross-legged, a position only ageing women will appreciate. Amongst the tears of laughter, Christine suggested they take a walk for ten yards to the next bus stop. At this moment it was evident that Jean needed a bladder operation! They ascended the bus which drew up within seconds. The girls had to compose themselves quickly.

"Look at us," Carole said, "We look like Minnie, May and Madge."

These were elderly relatives on Alan's side of the family, who had a reputation for making foolish mistakes. Their stories always raised the roof with laughter at any time.

"You can include Ena and Martha there," said Kath, struggling to control herself. "We're like the old women from Coronation Street forty years ago."

On the bus a manner of calmness was restored, but as Margaret paid the fares giddiness erupted once again, though their voices were lightened for the public's benefit.

"Oh five return fares to the City please." Money was exchanged. "Thank you, em, please can you tell me which bus we catch back?" enquired Margaret.

"Yes! this one," came the curt reply.

The answer was so obvious; the driver looked at her as though she was not all there.

The rest of the girls laughed until they were red in the face, cherry red, with trying to stifle this embarrassing cotton-picking laughter.

The locals did not recognise the broader Northern accent. They flashed looks at all five of them, as though they had roamed out from the backwater.

They alighted the bus at the station and tried to make a mental note of both the bus stand and the bus number. This sounds easy, but it proved to be more difficult for women approaching fifty. One can only blame those blasted hormones.

A famous store had an enormous sale. The girls invaded it as though they may never see clothes again. Anyone would think the four-minute warning had gone off, ordering people to their underground bunkers until the unforeseeable future. They all bought arms full, but Carole thought the plain white knickers were a great bargain, so she bought fifteen pairs, which raised more laughter.

Jean asked with a note of curiosity, "Why do you need all those?"

"Well you never know do you?" Carole chirped back. "I mean to say I bet you wouldn't mind borrowing a pair right now!"

In the heart of the City they were consumed by ethnicity, an outpouring of cosmopolitanism, as young people mingled without prejudice. Parents were educating their children on the important historic remains, confronted by the evidence of the survival of Roman traditional plumbing methods. The girls were captivated, and lingered until the late afternoon became darksome. After a little uncertainty they found the bus stand. Number 33 bus was docked in the dark with its driver seated, resting deservedly. Margaret and Carole also rested on a bench, tired and forlorn now after a hectic day. They swore the driver beckoned them onto his bus. They called for the others to join them, only to be refused entry to the bus. They were imagining things. All of them sat back down to weaker laughter, for they had lost their vibrancy. Finally, a bus was taking them along Newbridge Road to the *Haute Combe Hotel* which stood in illuminated splendour. The upside of fifty meant that they would all need to lie on their beds before taking a hot shower ready for dinner.

Arrangements were made for them to meet in the garage, where Christine and Margaret would partake in pre-dinner drinks. Eileen had recommended a cosy country pub just a few minutes walk from the hotel, yet on the edge of the riverbank.

Good hearty food was served, and conversation was reserved for family whilst they ate. Both Christine and Carole now had Justin and Keelie who were both married to loving partners, so Jean had a lot to catch up on. They hired a taxi back to the hotel shortly before 11:00 p.m. The journey felt like a trip in a sports car driving a Grand Prix circuit. It's a wonder they managed to hang onto their stomach contents.

Back in the garage the two occupants were consuming pre-bedtime whisky and cokes, whilst the others preferred tea or coffee. They all sprawled on the two double beds as laughter rang out once more.

"Yes, Eileen had the right idea," said Kath. "Could you imagine if we were in the main hotel making this racket?"

"Well," Margaret exploded, "that blooming Park and Ride, we must all be as thick as that wall there."

Christine said through joyful tears, "Well some things never change do they? What's the song we used to sing? *'Be young, be foolish but be happy.'*

"Da da doo doo, da doo doo," Jean sang in remembrance of the Mecca days.

Christine finished, "We might not be young in body, but one thing is for sure, we definitely are in mind and spirit."

Devilish laughter radiated like a great conductor of heat. Some time later, Jean, Kath and Carole felt it was time to turn in. They crept to their family room on the second floor. Jean chatted away until she was talking to herself, for both Kath and Carole were drifting into motionless sleep. The two drinkers carried on with their night-caps until their speech became gibberish. They fell into deep sleep, filling the room with grunting and snorting noises, which was another good reason for them to reside in the garage!

Breakfast, which compared more to brunch, was served in the traditional dining room on Sunday morning. The girls were quiet, recovering from the day and night before. Bags packed and bills settled they loaded up the car and drove into Bath for their final view of the city before meeting up with Barrie. The climate had changed overnight. It was cold and damp but they were unperturbed. Having parked the car on the multi-storey car park a discussion was had. They could not leave without a tour on the open top bus. They bartered with each bus company for the best deals. Once happy with the fare, they climbed up the stairs to the top deck, then tried to fathom the headphones and the radio network. They listened seriously to the fascinating history of how Queen Victoria visited the exquisite Georgian City. They were inspired by architectural delights of the Royal Crescent. Putney Bridge was amazing. During this informative tour Kath's face looked puzzled.

Christine nudged the others to watch her expression, "Can you not follow it Kath?" enquired Christine cheekily.

"Well no, not really, I could at first, but then I stopped to take a photograph and now it somehow doesn't seem to make any sense," Kath answered rather perplexed.

Laughter surfaced yet again, it appeared that Christine had changed the channel to Japanese, just to see how long it would take Kath to notice.

"You're worse than a child, Christine," scolded Kath, but then joined in the laughter.

This girlie get together had not only been good fun, but an enjoyable history lesson. The city tour bus served a dual purpose; if they spotted an interesting shop or store open then they would jump off and hop on again at their convenience, saving their middle-aged legs and feet from the aches and pains of walking.

Inevitably, it was time to meet Barrie and say a temporary goodbye to their friend Jean. The lean years were behind them now so they made a sort of pact. It was Carole's 50th birthday next in December 2001, so they would decide on another city and do the same thing. The girls were individuals, and their wonderful friendship could be picked up at anytime with any of them, sharing life's highs and lows, warmth and fears. They were like a set of pans all cooking on one ring.

The little green car ferried Kath, Christine, Margaret and Carole out of the valley up towards the M4. They were met with a blanket of fog. The clouds were almost burning them, and they felt claustrophobic, with visibility being down to ten yards.

"Well it's a right pea-souper is this, we'll never get home at this rate," complained Margaret.

As they approached the motorway the white shroud had resurrected, leaving just pinpricks of rain to be cleared by the windscreen wipers.

The conversation focused on what a good idea it had been to start celebrating half centuries. It was a bit like renewing baptismal promises, keeping the flame of friendship alight.

Nightfall came early, and Carole felt tired and drained driving on the unlit motorway. She would welcome the sign for her home town of Burnley. As they grew closer to home Margaret agreed to ring Jean for her reassurance of arriving home safely. Carole saw each of her pals to their doors. They all thanked each other for such a good time as they waved bye-bye.

On entering her own home Carole dumped her bags in the hall, weary from the journey. She stood at the living-room door and in a tired voice said, "Oh, I just need a cup of tea or maybe something stronger!"

Alan turned and beckoned her to come and sit down. "We've had some bad news," he said quietly and gently.

The year hadn't started well, but she prepared herself for more bad news. Listening to Alan repeat the telephone call from friends abroad announcing tragic news was all too much. She held her head in her hands and cried. They all cried, Alan, Dominic and twenty-one year old Melissa. The news was too tragic for script.

Chapter Twenty-Two

Three days later, the fragility of life hit Carole, Alan and their three children like a sudden slap across the face. She was at work one day then Carole found herself lying seriously ill in a hospital bed in the early hours of the morning. Muffled voices pounded her head, human shadows drifted around her. She could not comprehend exactly what was happening. Later in the afternoon she was visited by the Consultant who asked to speak to her family.

Her family returned, and Philip her father, who was now seventy-years old, sat forcing an incongruous smile. Alan, whose eyes looked bluer than ever, filled with pools eager to spill, and Melissa's tears had already begun to fall. The doctor could not offer any guarantees. Some survived Pancreatitis, but ten percent of people did not. It would be some time before the critical period passed. It all depended upon how Carole's body responded to the onslaught of crucial antibiotics.

It was two weeks before she turned the corner, although she was in danger until the offending gallbladder had been removed. All sorts of complications were expected to set in.

Amongst all the gravity of the situation as often happens in such times, laughter often finds a place. Kath would visit after her ward work, as would Keelie and Melissa, Carole's daughters, who both worked at the hospital.

One evening Christine brought Margaret to visit, "Well those fifteen pairs of knickers came in handy, I reckon you had a premonition of all this."

The gloomy faces around the bed lightened as the atmosphere became suddenly easier.

After four weeks Carole was allowed home for a few days, then had to return for surgery. She had been allocated a different bed within the same bay. Sleep overtook her on the day of her operation.

It was whilst she was sleeping that her son Dominic came to visit. A deplorable genetic illness had recently robbed him of most of his sight. He could only identify his mother's bed by the deep turquoise dressing gown hanging by the bed. Dominic made himself comfortable in the armchair normally reserved for patients. Deciding it unwise to waken his mum, he too drifted into slumber. He woke suddenly unaware of his surroundings. Kindly the family of another patient offered him a lift home, for which he was exceedingly grateful. It was another hour before Carole awoke.

A young girl had been admitted in the bed across. Coincidentally, she worked at the same firm as Dominic. It was Gail who told her of his struggle to find his mum. It was at this precise moment Carole became aware of the amount of stress she and her family had been bombarded with, and her inability to recognise that things could not change. Two days later Dominic bought her a book, *'Yoga for Softies'*. This would be her strategy for combating life's unrelenting pressures and tensions.

Chapter Twenty-Three

It was mid-May when Carole went into work to speak to Maureen Payne, her Manager and family friend, about weaning herself back into work. She sat facing the open window. The noise of the traffic was intrusive, though revving and slowing of motor engines was unavoidable at peak times. The air was bustling with such sounds as well as pedestrians, as there were parents and scholars from neighbouring schools chattering about their day. Four o'clock always brought an upsurge of noise. The weather was overcast but unremarkable. Still the tree-lined avenue in full foliage where the hospital stood, gave the busy road a vision of up-market sophistication.

It was agreed that Carole would return to work in June for three days a week, working six-hour shifts. Her illness had left her psychologically a little disturbed. She felt an urgent need to be around family and close friends, those people she cherished most. The home she loved became a cocoon, a protective shell. But she knew living in the shadow of her own mother that she carried the same gene responsible for depression. Great efforts had to be made when stuck in her darkest thoughts, not to let this rogue gene drag her down the same bottomless pit, as it had done with Audrey.

Carole had been drawn to visiting places and pursuits she had enjoyed with her family in previous years. She reflected on pleasurable photographs, and became somewhat phobic to work. After five months the surroundings seemed less familiar, casting doubts in her confidence and ability to serve the people in her care.

Once Maureen had helped her come to a decision, Carole left the office and walked the short distance to Deerplay Ward where she worked. She met one of the sisters where they sat discussing a plan of action for her return. A commotion broke out.

It was Maureen whom she had just left, her face displaying shock, her voice conveyed fear. "Carole," she said, her hands moving in a calming manner, "Don't panic but I think you should come quickly. I thought that you might have left…"

Carole stopped her mid-sentence, "What do you mean?"

"Let me just tell you," Maureen explained, "Your Christine has had an accident, I've just seen and heard it from my office. Her car is embedded in a tree. The airbag came up and everything. She must be in the Accident and Emergency Department. I've sent Debbie across to see how she is?"

"OH NO!" Carole shouted as she quickly made her way from the ward to Casterton Avenue.

At the scene she found her sister's shoes. In the Accident and Emergency Department she sought Christine, who was in shock, but relatively unscathed.

Carole had been given the task of informing Peter, Christine's husband, and meeting Lucy their daughter from her workplace.

Christine had recently been diagnosed with hypertension, it was spotted when she went for a pre-assessment for surgery for a hysterectomy. The operation was to be postponed until her blood pressure was stable enough for the anaesthetic, even if it was to be lowered by the use of medication. Christine was unaware that she had high blood pressure, her body must have been compensating somewhere. Work had been busy and demanding, and although she thrived on this, she had felt more tired lately, but she'd just put it down to being anaemic, and thought that this would be corrected once she had her operation. Meantime she had just started on new medication to resolve this. The theory was she blacked out at the wheel of the car, hitting a tree. Mercifully no one else was hurt, though there were children close by, a tragedy had thankfully been narrowly averted.

The accident required Christine to be admitted for tests, as all other explanations for the blackout had to be ruled out. Was it a faint or a fit, or the medication? At this stage no one could be sure. All this trauma had happened on the Thursday, the problem being that Peter and Christine had a schedule to meet. They were taking a long-haul flight to Mexico for a well-earned vacation.

With much persuasion the medical team granted her permission to travel. It was months before her blood pressure was stabilised with the help of corrective medication, and many valuable working hours were lost. This perplexed Christine, for being a full-time housewife tormented her. Her mind was becoming frugal, she thrived on challenges and felt deprived.

The intervening months passed while both sisters tried to speed up their recovery. Carole found herself back in work in early June as planned. Kath, whose health always seemed to be on the brink with one thing or another, had just applied for, and was accepted as an auxiliary nurse on Deerplay Ward, where the two sisters worked. If anyone had asked thirty years ago where the girls' destiny lay, they would never have guessed, but as fate would have it, this is where they were now at this moment in time, side by side, working within their own capacities.

Chapter Twenty-Four

August approached once more as time rapidly moved on at hair-raising speed. Jean was in Burnley for her yearly jaunt with friends and family. She made her customary visit to Mrs. Hand's, one place she would never miss. Unfortunately only Carole and Margaret were able to see her on this occasion. Christine was away on yet another holiday abroad with Peter, and Kath and Mick had met up with friends at a caravan meeting.

It was an idyllic summer's evening, so the three girls drove out to a quaint country pub in Fence, one of the outlying villages North of Burnley. The food was delicious, the company satisfying. It was always good to catch up with Jean. But instead of the usual laughter, illness dominated the conversation.

"I've been for my bladder op," said Jean, in a disappointing tone.

"Well that's good isn't it?" asked Carole.

"No, not really, they'd done the necessary repair, but found pre-cancerous cells."

"Bloody hell!" exclaimed Margaret.

"I know," Jean replied, "Can't believe it can you, since we've turned fifty we've all been proper poorly; frightening isn't it? Still they've started treatment now and they'll see me in six months. I'm in good hands; they've been marvellous at the hospital. And guess what? Adam gave me a beautiful bunch of flowers, and you know he said, "I love you mum".

"Makes you want to cry doesn't it?"

"Yes," Carole joined in, "illness is life-changing isn't it? You realise what and who matters, and your whole outlook changes."

They had eaten a gourmet meal along with many others out enjoying a mid-week break, now it was 10:15 p.m. and time to drive home. Two of them had to be up for work early in the morning, and Jean's sister Maureen had planned a trip to the market town of Skipton.

From the porch of the Bay Horse the sounds of thunder and angry rain echoed. They made a dash to the car, but sat in the car park for a little while waiting for the rain to ease off. Ten minutes they waited, during which time they moaned to each other about life and living with teenagers, the amount of washing they created and all that sort of thing before driving back to Burnley via the by-pass. Although the sky was low, grey and dull, the green pasturage seemed to be truly emerald. Jean commented on how the North always seems to have unpredictable rain, but even so God granted this little corner of England a generous amount of natural beauty.

"I'd like to go to Oxford, you know, to see how the literacy folk live," announced Carole, thinking out loud.

"That's a bit out of the blue," Margaret remarked, "What's brought this on?"

"I don't know. I was just admiring the landscape, but I imagine Oxford to be extremely picturesque."

Margaret was quick to answer, "Bloody hell have you swallowed a dictionary?"

"Well if everyone is in agreement we can go for my birthday do," Carole said emphatically.

"Yes okay," Jean chirped in, "but how about we stay for two nights?"

"Yeh, and I think we will be better on the train. The last journey nearly put your lights out Carole," put in Margaret.

"Yes, you're right," Carole agreed, thinking of her own welfare. "I'll speak to Christine and Kath then we'll get it sorted."

They all agreed that after Christmas would be better than before. Jean went on to explain that Adam would be twenty-one in January, and Claire eighteen within the same week, and so they were having a joint celebration party. Mid-February would be the ideal time.

Carole volunteered to book the train for the four of them from Burnley. Jean did not think she would have a problem travelling from Bournemouth. They'd look for a good deal on accommodation, hopefully with a little luxury, seeing as how they were staying for two nights.

Jean and Barrie left Burnley behind once more. Within weeks the third season of the year had arrived like a secret messenger revealing her rustic colours slowly, but defiantly, as leaves were left scattered lightly on the ground.

Chapter Twenty-Five

The day to day routine continued uninterrupted. Margaret owned a sequence that ticked along like clockwork. Four evenings a week, Monday, Tuesday, Saturday and Sunday at 6:00 p.m. sharp, she visited her mother, taking her meals for the following days. Mrs. Hand was now housebound, but was quite capable of pottering around her little bungalow, which was less than five minute's walk from her daughter's home.

Sometimes one of the girls would be there, quite often it was Kath, as Mick her husband, worked away from home driving heavy goods lorries to their destination. They'd watch the soaps together, predicting where and how each drama would finish. Before leaving at eight, Margaret would prepare Mrs. Hand's medicinal hot toddy.

"Helps me sleep," she'd say, justifying her nightly tipple.

Margaret very rarely arrived home to Colin before 9:30 p.m. as she had a rally of friends to call upon socially on her way back from her mother's. There were four people in particular that she devotedly offered her company to in turn.

Monday nights were reserved for Shirley, who lived directly opposite Margaret and Colin. There was just a narrow cobbled backstreet, and twelve feet of concrete yard, housing a tool shed, recycled from a converted outside toilet, and washing lines, wheelie bins and pot plants to separate them. There was one advantage though; keeping a neighbourly lookout, guarding and protecting their collective possessions, was the reassurance that each could identify with.

Shirley's husband Ken, worked away from home, and she was more than grateful for Margaret's company. Being softly sensitive, yet holding a chubby personality, Shirley slotted in nicely with Margaret's ever-growing composition of friends.

Rita, at 23, Richmond Street was also on Margaret's list of people to visit. Being seventy-years old she chatted about life in the good old days. She talked and talked of St. Mary Magdalene's school in the 1930's and 40's.

Then there was Margaret with the dodgy knee at number 5; her husband was now deceased, he was Italian. The older Margaret, entertained her namesake friend, with fascinating tales of her in-laws and their Mediterranean lifestyle.

There was no forgetting Marjorie, who would bring all her neighbours, including Kathleen Lord from the shop, together for gourmet suppers.

Colin didn't mind, or think any less that his wife wasn't always around. His meal was ready on the table when he returned from a day's work.

If any of the girls called asking for her he'd invariably inform the caller, "Oh she's out on her mission, visiting the sick!"

Colin had no time for life's material wealth or possessions, but he valued the rich knowledge he gained from being an avid reader. He would absorb his broadsheet newspaper from front to back daily. Privacy and dignity, and of course his beloved Margaret, were for him the finer things in life. This knowledge came to the fore on Wednesday evenings when he and Michael, Kathleen Lord's husband, and Wilkie his mate, took themselves off to the Clough for their weekly fun quiz. Colin had the mind of an encyclopaedia. No other team stood a chance of collecting the cash prize whilst Colin and his team, *'The Three Amigos'* were in force.

Margaret took advantage of her husband's absence on these evenings, talking for hours on the telephone to friends she hadn't seen for a while. Jean in Bournemouth being one of them!

Chapter Twenty-Six

"How much weight have you lost?" Christine enquired as she followed Margaret through the hallway and into the back room of 1, Richmond Street.

It was Wednesday afternoon and the girls were catching up on the latest news whilst having a well-earned cup of coffee.

Margaret, who had just finished work at Kathleen's shop answered her nonchalantly. "I've just been cutting down that's all, and besides I've not lost that much."

Christine disagreed and said what she thought, "You must have lost a fair bit, because your skirt is hanging off you. I wish I could get into the mood for dieting, I just don't seem to have the willpower these days."

Christine pondered, she had counted the calories many times, tried all different faddy diets, but Margaret never did. She did not want to lose weight, and constantly told Christine to get off that stupid diet and just eat normally.

As if to prove a point Margaret produced two chocolate wafer biscuits with the coffee, and both of them tucked in and began to discuss the events which had taken place since they last met. They discussed the forthcoming trip to Oxford, where they would meet up with Jean.

It was taken for granted that both Margaret and Christine would share the same room; they had the most in common. They liked to stay up late and drink the same whisky and coke; they also laughed at the same jokes and teasingly bossed the others about. So they planned what they would take with them, and what fun they would have.

Christine had lived around the corner from Richmond Street for the best part of nineteen years, so it was easy for her to pop into Margaret's on her day off. If one week Christine did not show, Margaret always wanted to know why? Both Kath and Carole also called up to see Margaret, usually after work, they would sometimes go on a Wednesday evening for a chilli supper. Margaret only called at Christine's if she had walked up to the post office, which was at the bottom of Scott Park Road; she preferred people to call at *her* house. She could prepare Colin's tea whilst they talked, as he came home from work at four-thirty and requested an early tea.

"I can't swallow this," meaning the pastry of a meat pie, which she held in her hands, Margaret said to Christine, whilst they were waiting in Kathleen's shop just before Margaret finished for the day. It was winter time and very cold, Christine was on her usual visit to Margaret's for afternoon coffee and a chat.

"Well, how long has this been going on?" Christine demanded from her friend.

"Oh, I don't know, a while, it's the pastry, it gets stuck in my throat." Margaret appeared unperturbed, but was annoyed because it was a nuisance. "In fact," she carried on, "I can't swallow other things, like toast. But it's funny because I can eat cream crackers."

Feeling concerned, Christine told Margaret that she ought to go to see the doctor.

"Um, I might," Margaret mumbled; she was not one for ailments, that is apart from her feet, which were badly damaged through working in damp conditions. She regularly visited the chiropodist, although if truth be known she carried on going for the pampering which it entailed.

Christine nagged her a few days later about going to the doctors, and Margaret informed her that she had already booked an appointment. This in itself gave Christine some concern, as it showed that Margaret was actually worried. What she did not do was tell Christine that she felt the condition had worsened, as there appeared to be more stodgy foods which she could not always digest. She had confirmed her worries to this friend only, although Kathleen Lord knew that Margaret struggled to eat pastry, because they often had their lunch together whilst working, although Carole, Kath and Jean were not aware. However all the girls agreed that more weight was dropping off Margaret.

When Carole approached her about her weight loss Margaret informed her that she was only using tea plates, and so the portions would be smaller. In fact, she said that Christine should do the same and she too would lose some weight!

Chapter Twenty-Seven

Unusually Christmas plodded by, and Christine, Carole and Jean took great pleasure in waving farewell to 2001. Their *annus horibilus*! The winter wasn't deep but fair and mild. There were no lamenting gale-force winds or drifting wadded snow. January and early February just brought days of formidable coloured shades of pewter, whereby Burnley's natural lofty contours were mostly hidden in mist, but gratification was sought from the promising sights of springtime. An array of snowdrops peeped out like gems awaiting discovery. Rare days dawned to lawns coated in dew, which had magically turned to a white icing of frost.

It was on one such day that the girls were travelling to Oxford to meet up with their friend Jean. It seemed to be a specially hand-picked day, when the sun was high and the sky an extra sharp blue, almost as sharp as ice itself. Yet again the little green car picked up the passengers, as Carole drove to Preston Railway Station on that Friday morning. The car was parked awaiting the journey back to Burnley on Sunday evening. First class train tickets had been booked at an astonishingly low price of £21.00 per person return.

They travelled in the front carriage in the lap of luxury, positioned alongside men and women who wore smartly tailored suits as an emblem of professionalism. Christine sat with Margaret, whilst Kath and Carole occupied the seats behind them. Dressed in smart coats and flowing scarves the girls looked nothing less than first class professional women themselves embracing travel.

The train moved out of Preston station in a rickety fashion, leaving urbanisation behind. Fun and folly started as the carriages peeled through hidden valleys and open countryside. Delightful snacks of smoked salmon with cream cheese and chives on bagels were served along with the usual quota of whisky and coke for the drinkers, whilst Carole and Kath stayed with the fine wine. They were all very dignified until Carole had a desperate urge to use the toilet. Three times she came back to her seat laughing like a hyena, unable to open the toilet door! Christine had little choice but to get up and operate the simple device. Once inside, Carole had to sit on the loo with her arm outstretched to keep the door shut. She couldn't fathom out how to lock it! On her way back to her seat business men peered above spectacles flashing distasteful looks.

In less than three hours the train streamed into Oxford Station, *'the historic city of dreaming spires'*. After alighting the carriage they made their way to the main concourse, and all eyes were on the lookout for Jean, who was due to have arrived twenty minutes earlier.

"Right get your phone out Carole. We'll give her a ring," said Christine.

Out came the 'brick', not her phone but the filofax.

"I don't believe it," snapped Christine. "You still haven't got Jean's number in your phone!"

Worse still, on opening her diary, Carole remembered that she had taken the page out with Jean's address and phone number on, just to save carrying the brick around.

"Oh blooming heck! I've left the page at home," gasped Carole not believing her own stupidity.

"What's she like?" said Margaret, "dementia's setting in already, so much for being fifty!"

It soon became obvious that the phone number was no longer needed, for amongst a medley of voices in conversation Jean could be heard. She could *always* be heard before she was seen. Not surprisingly she had found a lonely traveller willing to listen whilst she awaited her friends. They all met, bestowing hugs and kisses, whilst making their way to a taxi rank which stood opposite a metal jungle of bicycles.

The five girls joined the line of patrons waiting to hire a taxi. The people in the queue appeared affluent, as well as learned. Oxford being a city of fine culture, symphonic poetry seemed to echo onto its periphery. They had to keep their cool and remember where they were, but overexcitement always seemed to spark instant fits of giggles. Their turn arrived to board a cab. Hysterics broke out when all five of them had to magically make themselves super slim in order to share the same car.

Kath was first in, along with her double-sized suitcase. Christine and Margaret followed, then Carole squeezed onto the edge of the seat. They couldn't see each other for luggage, and Jean wasn't even in yet! Onlookers stared in amazement.

"There's room for a small bag here in the front," said the cab driver.

So Jean tried to sit there. "There isn't a seat," she cried whilst simultaneously trying to sit on the floor.

"I said a bag, not you," the impatient driver announced.

Her friends screamed in frivolous excitement. Having made her way to the rear door Jean was squashed to a pulp, and just about able to place her rump on the end of the pull-down, cinema-type seat to share with Carole. The crowd in the taxi rank had surely been freely amused with this live performance during the few minutes it took for the girls to get inside. From that moment there was no doubt the weekend was going to be another barrel of fun!

They had all noticed the weight loss Margaret now displayed. It was evident here in Oxford because she brought with her a new wardrobe. There was only one room ready when they arrived at the *Four Pillars Hotel,* so the girls made themselves comfy in it. Margaret decided that this room would be hers and Christine's. They began to unpack, whilst the goodies of champagne and hand-made chocolates, which Peter had brought back for them from one of his work trips to Belgium, were passed around. The trouble was that the bottle would not open. For some reason Carole thought it would be a good idea to open it with her teeth, not realising what could happen if the cork backfired into her throat. The girls were laughing and screaming at her to remove the bottle from her mouth.

When Christine opened her suitcase Margaret spied the burgundy silk nightie.

"What are you doing with that? I've bought you one."

Christine removed the offending ankle-length garment to show Margaret, as she was given a carrier bag which contained the shortened version.

"I had to get you one, they only had our size and they were selling them off at £2.00," Margaret informed them all.

The others pleaded, "Where's our present?"

"Oh, you don't share our room. Margaret always brings me a little treat, don't you?" Christine mimicked like a small child.

"I only bring something to go with our nightcap," justified Margaret.

Sunday arrived far too early. As if to delay their departure, Margaret suggested they make plans for Christine and Kath's 50th birthday celebrations.

"I don't even want to think about turning fifty," said Kath in a high voice. "I don't celebrate birthdays, you're as old as you feel, that's my motto."

Margaret was swift to return with, "That maybe so, but you've no choice in this one. You're next. What's the date? November 23rd, and Christine's a month later at Christmas. Might as well have a joint do. Who fancies Stratford-upon-Avon?"

Kath and Christine glanced at one another, as did Jean and Carole. "Yeh, okay," everyone seemed to echo in mutual agreement. In fact, they clapped their hands with glee like children at a party. Carole thought it might be a good idea to go late November or early December in order to combine it with a chance for Xmas shopping, so she clapped even harder at this thought. One thought soon led to another.

She declared out loud, "I'll tell you what, after a weekend of self-entertainment, I think we could all do with Jean's bladder operation before Stratford."

Jean raised her hand and voice in merriment. Everyone else crossed their legs as giggling they seconded the motion.

Two o'clock was time to wave goodbye to Oxford and Jean. The girls travelling North felt uneasy at leaving Jean on her own, as her train to Bournemouth was not due to arrive until twenty minutes past two.

"Don't worry," said Christine, "she'll soon find some poor soul to natter to."

"Yeh, that's the trouble," Kath put in cautiously, "she could be talking to anybody!"

As they trundled their way across the overhead bridge to platform eight, they dropped lumbering bags and suitcases, turned to stand, moving hands to and fro, like long fragrant grasses swaying in the wind, bidding farewell to Jean who grinned and waved frantically back to them. Her arms and hands gathered up to twice the speed, as though to make up for her lack in numbers.

They didn't hang around on platform eight for long, as their train pulled in on time, but to their disgust there were only four carriages, instead of the much needed eight.

From platform six Jean could see passengers already standing. Chuckling to herself she thought of the boastful way her friends had described the pleasurable journey down. "I didn't get any of that," she'd said with a fraction of resentment. Right now, she wondered whether it might be her turn for a little splendour on her homeward-bound journey? The girls had made sure Jean had a drink and a sandwich for her trip home.

"We're okay," said Margaret, "we've got a meal and drinks included."

"Yeh, we're all inclusive," laughed Christine.

Everyone on platform eight scrambled into the carriages. Any thoughts of grandeur were immediately dispelled, as all thoughts of an all inclusive service were just an illusion now. There was a mad scramble for seats. Some people obligingly squeezed up to allow others to share, whilst others stood holding onto seats and overhead rails. The girls were separated; Kath and Carole had to stand. All their hopes and expectations of luxury travel had vanished. This was going to be a long, miserable journey.

As the four carriages ambled begrudgingly out of Oxford station a male teenager, (probably a student on his way home), gave up his seat for Carole and Kath to share. Another followed suit, showing good manners by standing to allow another young woman to be seated. At each station folks alighted, and new people boarded. The whole fiasco resembled a cattle train.

Seats were shuffled, until eventually the friends were seated together. They nudged up, making themselves as small and as tight as a concertina, to allow an elderly gentleman with a ruddy face revealing his ill-health, to perch on the end of the upholstery. A young girl of about eighteen, with her arm in a sling boarded at the next station. A man at the far end of the vehicle kindly offered her his seat, but the girl shyly declined the gesture, embarrassed by the sympathetic attention her injury had somehow gained.

On the journey down to Oxford the carriages had been orderly, clean and refreshed. The pillar-box red upholstery, had reflected warmth and a glow of excitement, but now the train was in mayhem. Carole made a meagre attempt to visit the toilet, but gave it up as a bad job. Young students with bags and baggage flooded the floor. This was 21st Century public transport, but it reflected a war-torn, Third World country.

The odour was rank, with too many smelly bodies forced together in such a confined space. Darkened, dank satanic buildings, amid a storm of boiling cloud-filled skies were the view from the vapour-covered windows as the locomotive drifted through the 'Black Country'. Now sadly lost were the flowery signs of early spring.

At Birmingham station a lean, willowy girl, possibly in her twenties with her guide-dog, an ever obedient Labrador, boarded. Her eyes, deep-set and closed, appeared to see nothing, not even shadows, just the deepest emptiness. She had dressed with flair. A long dark winter coat covered her down to her ankles. A rich velvet scarf of autumnal colours, draped her shoulders. Her black lusty-glazed thatch of hair was brushed back and fastened into a pony-tail.

Carole felt a thrust of empathy. Immediately she tapped the girl on her arm. "Here, have this seat, you can squeeze on the end, here."

"No, no, really, I am okay," came the reply.

Maybe by Carole being vocal, the girl understood the person offering the seat to be approximately twice her age. The young woman's worthiness, respect and excellence in manner was undeniable, even touching. Carole, Christine, Kath and Margaret looked at this remarkable person with contemplation and recounted all their blessings.

But what was shameful, was that three rows further down the carriage was a mother, a well-educated looking woman in her late thirties, with her two sons of junior school age occupying three seats. People glared at their disrespectfulness. The mother's arrogance and ignorance were so briskly apparent. They disapproved of the lack of social skills and the manners of her sons. During the last few miles of her journey the mother was shamed into shifting the boys together and sharing seats.

They expressed their annoyance like spoilt puppies, growling and snarling, "Why do we have to travel like this mummy, I am so uncomfortable," said one of the boys. His vowels and consonants revealing perfect elocution.

The mother answered her son in perfect English, "I am afraid everyone is uncomfortable darling, but it will not be for much longer now as we are nearly home."

Returning from Oxford for Christine was the beginning of a new chapter for her and her family, because they had just bought a new house after being in Scott Park Road for over nineteen years. It had been the right time to move to a smaller house now that the family were leaving home. They had bought a quasi-town house with a garden on the edge of the park, quite near to Justin and Amanda, near to Carole and Alan, and very close by to Keelie, her niece. The family spent two weeks living with Justin and Amanda whilst they could move into their house. The date for moving coincided with the trip to Oxford, but Peter insisted that Christine should still go and he would move in with the help of Justin, Alex and Lucy.

Chapter Twenty-Eight

Margaret's doctor wisely ordered an investigation called a barium x-ray, which should locate any blockage of the oesophagus, the track which takes fluid and food down into the stomach. This was arranged for the following week, which alerted the girls, if not Margaret and Colin. April 12th was the day when Christine took her friend Margaret to the hospital for this procedure. A busman's holiday perhaps for Christine, but she was off work herself as she was due to be admitted for her impending surgery. As soon as she appeared in the hospital gown, the amount of weight loss that Margaret showed was quite shocking, even to someone who knew that she had lost a lot of weight. Seeing her skin hanging loosely from the tops of her arms and around her neck forced Christine into silence.

It was Margaret who spoke first, "Will you be able to come in with me?" she asked.

Christine said that she would ask the assistant.

"Margaret Fort?" shouted the assistant radiographer.

Making herself known, she asked, "Can my friend come in with me, she's a nurse?"

"No, sorry," was the curt reply.

The friends just exchanged glances, letting each other know that they would still be together. What appeared to be only seconds later, but in reality could not have been, Margaret emerged from the treatment room.

Christine's heart fell down to her feet and asked her friend, "Did they not do it?"

"Yes," Margaret replied, her voice light and airy, "I only needed to drink a little bit of the rotten stuff, come on let's go for our coffee so I can get rid of this horrible taste. We'll go to Barden Mill, shall we?"

They did not go to the mill as planned, as they walked through the main out-patient waiting area Margaret suggested that they have a coffee there, then go home. And that's just what they did. Neither said very much on the way home. Christine wanted to know exactly what was said once the radiographer had finished.

Margaret said rather annoyed, "I've told you, not much, I've got to go back to my doctors at the beginning of next week."

In Christine's mind was the reality of the diagnosis which she had feared, and she knew if Margaret asked her anything she would expect truthful answers. But she wondered if she would be able to do this for her?

During this anxious wait the girls kept each other company by telephone or calling at Margaret's house after work. Kath never said at this stage if she suspected the worst scenario, but both Carole and Christine had seen this before with a dear friend of both their husband's, and so were quite concerned.

Margaret was told by her doctor that she had a blockage of some kind, and it would need to be viewed with an endoscope, which is a camera attached to a long tube that is passed through the throat and into the stomach. A biopsy would be obtained at the same time.

On April 22nd Christine took Margaret for this procedure. There was a choice given as to whether the patient had a local anaesthetic applied to the back of the throat or intravenous sedation. Margaret did not get the option owing to some expected difficulty in passing the tube, and so came to inform Christine who was in the waiting room. The nurse also came and told her that it would be at least two o'clock before Margaret would be ready to go home. Christine telephoned Kath and Carole to keep them both up to date, but Carole was not in.

The telephone's shrill tones interrupted Christine's thoughts, it was only 12:50 p.m. so it would not be the hospital. However it was, the nurse was asking her to get here as soon as she could, as although Margaret was not quite ready to go home, the doctor had some bad news to tell her and he would like her to have someone with her when he spoke to her.

Adrenalin rushed through Christine's body, she knew exactly what the doctor was going to tell Margaret, she knew it would be cancer, she just felt it.

The first thing she found herself doing was dialling Kath's telephone number. "Kath, be at the door in two minutes, the nurse has rung, it's bad news they've asked me to get there quick. Ring Carole while I set off," ordered Christine.

Kath had expressed a wish to go with Christine to collect their friend. Ready and waiting Kath got in the car and they somehow drove in silence, other than quietly agreeing to each other that it would be cancer. The car practically abandoned, they raced to be at their friend's side, though Carole was still not in.

A nurse was with Margaret, the doctor couldn't wait, so he told Margaret that she had cancer of the upper gastric tract. She would probably have it removed within the next two weeks, following more investigations.

"It's cancer!" was all she said.

Her two friends just knelt down beside a seated Margaret, who looked like she could have shed some tears but was trying to deny this with her dry eyes at present. They both took her hands and squeezed her, being ever so strong and not crying, for how could they when Margaret wasn't?

"Right what's next?" Margaret demanded from the nurse.

Giving Margaret a piece of paper with the name of the cancer specialist nurse, she told her that soon she would be seeing the Consultant Surgeon and he would probably perform surgery and remove the tumour. There would be blood tests and a CT Scan first, so that when the appointment arrives, the surgeon had everything to hand. It would be in about two to three weeks.

"Right that's it then, come on let's go to Christine's and get hold of Carole," Margaret said flatly.

"I'll get the car, Kath you and Margaret wait at the door," was Christine's reply.

The journey home was mostly silent. On arrival, Carole was still not in.

Margaret asked Christine some more questions, some of which she could give honest answers to, and others which she had no answers for.

"Try Carole again," Margaret suggested.

At last she was in.

"Where have you been, we've been trying for ages to get hold of you. Margaret and Kath are here, come round the kettle's just boiled," Christine half-shouted at Carole.

"I've got cancer!" Margaret told Carole as she walked through the kitchen.

Everyone looked at each other. Carole and Kath, whose tears could no longer be held back, let them slide down their sad faces.

"You can stop that you two," demanded Margaret. "I'll fight it, I'll have the surgery in two weeks, then I'll be okay. They must have caught it soon. I've not had to wait for anything."

That day dawned for the beginning of Margaret's fight for her life. As they drank coffee and ate biscuits, each of them harboured different thoughts; not talking, just going through the motion of trying to act normally.

Margaret spoke first, following the silent coffee break. "You'll have to come with me to tell my mother," she announced.

All four of them had been thinking about Mrs. Hand; how she would cope with the news, and how she would manage without her daughter being able to go to her house all the time?

"You two can't come like that snivelling. Christine will take me," Margaret instructed.

Although Christine was devastated by the news, she had prepared herself for this by shedding tears earlier in the morning, so she was now able to move about on automatic pilot. Margaret expected this from her, as she was outwardly a strong person like herself, who presently appeared to be in control, and although she came down hard on Carole and Kath for their tears, she also knew it was too much for them.

"Time to go," Margaret smiled as she left.

Christine drove Margaret to the little bungalow on Harold Street to an anxiously waiting Mrs. Hand; whose only **real** daughter was going to break both the bad news, and her heart.

Meanwhile, Carole and Kath sat in Carole's car and cried together. It opened a gateway for Kath to talk to Carole about losing her mum. In all the years that the girls had known each other, Kath could not freely talk about the loss of her mum until now. Carole, ever the eager listener, let Kath spill out all her buried feelings and unspoken words from so long ago. Kath and Carole left Christine's home with bloated, blotchy faces from their unrestrained tears.

"I'll take you home," said Carole. "Just look at us, we look dreadful, I don't know what folk will think if anyone sees us like this?"

"I know," sobbed Kath. "but I always had this dream – this vision, without sounding awful, but because Michael and Colin are a good few years older, I always thought they would die first and that Margaret and I would live together. She would do the cooking, and I would do the cleaning. I've never liked cooking and Margaret loves it. Do you know what I mean? Well I never expected this."

"Well," Carole took hold of Kath's hand, "let's not go down that road yet. Alan's Uncle John was diagnosed with the same illness, and he lived for fifteen years after that. Having said all that, something niggling at the back of my mind tells me Margaret won't have the operation!"

"You don't think she'd refuse do you?" murmured Kath.

"No, its not that," Carole spoke slowly, "I just can't imagine her in intensive care with all that monitoring. Anyway, let's just hope, for where there's life, there's always hope! Come on let's get home," said Carole, starting up the engine.

"Are you all right love?" Mrs. Hand gently asked her daughter.

Margaret and Christine looked at each other.

"You've been a long time, I've been phoning you, but you weren't in," she continued.

"I've got cancer," Margaret said very flatly. "But don't you go worrying yourself, I'm having some more tests, and then in about two week's time I'm having it removed. I've been back a while; we've all just been to Christine's for a brew."

Mrs. Hand did not need to ask who ALL were, she knew it was the girls. "Christine, will she be okay love?" Mrs. Hand enquired.

Christine nodded and said, "Let's all hope so, everything is happening quickly, so we have to wait and see what the doctor says."

Neither of them sat down. They both kissed Mrs. Hand goodbye, with Margaret saying that she would not be calling that evening, but she would be there the following night. Carole and Kath had planned to visit Mrs. Hand later that evening to make sure that she was all right.

"Next stop," Margaret told Christine, "is Kathleen's. She'll have to know, because I'm not going to be working again."

They walked into the shop together. Kathleen Lord was weighing some peas ready to be bagged up, and she stopped suddenly to look at them. It seemed to Christine unfair of Margaret to blurt out to Kathleen that she had cancer. Tears filled her eyes and overflowed onto her rosy, weathered cheeks. With hindsight, it was Margaret's coping mechanism, to give an air of matter-of-fact, showing no trace of emotion.

"You go and put the kettle on, I'll bring your groceries," said Christine.

And for once Margaret obeyed the order without question.

Christine put an arm on Kathleen and told her the expected plans. When Kathleen apologised for crying Christine said, "It's okay Kathleen, I'm so sorry she told you as she did, she did not need to do that."

"Yes she did," Kathleen said, "she's trying to protect me, trying to make it seem less than what it is. What will I do? We're like 'Derby and Joan', we're like an old married couple, we laugh, cry, argue and banter with each other. We've worked together for so long. And the four of us are good friends," meaning Michael, Kathleen's husband and Colin.

When Christine returned with the groceries she informed Margaret that Kathleen was upset.

"I know," agreed Margaret, "Colin's rung."

"You haven't told him over the phone, have you?"

"Yeh, he asked me, so I told him."

"Margaret, why didn't you wait, he'll be home in an hour?"

She did not answer, just lifted her shoulders.

Ryan came bouncing in, "All right mum? Hiya Christine."

Here we go again, thought Christine, she did not know how many more times she could hear this. Feeling sorry only for herself because she knew she would go through it all again with Peter and her children, and not forgetting Philip, her dad. He had become very fond of Margaret over the years. His persona had mellowed, he no longer was the tyrant of his youth, coping with the pressures of financial difficulties with a young family to support. He was a right grand old chap now.

"I've got a tumour Ryan; I need an operation to remove it," Margaret endorsed.

"Oh good, at least it isn't the Big C," he chirped.

The two women held a silent gaze.

"It is cancer Ryan, the tumour is cancer," Margaret told her son very gently.

"Right, I'm going home now Margaret," said Christine. "I'll leave you and Ryan together and Colin will be home soon."

Margaret stood up lightly as if a great weight had been lifted. She kissed her friend saying that she would phone her later that night. Once home, Christine relayed the day's events to Peter, who just held her tightly, knowing that there wasn't much he could say to take her pain away, but letting her know that he was there for her.

Christine's children would need to know, but not tonight, she would tell them tomorrow.

The next event for Carole, was to break the news to Alan and their three children. Margaret had always figured in their lives like an aunty. Then she had to digest the thoughts of ringing Jean. Her stomach churned as it had many years ago at junior school, just before a caning. She rehearsed in her mind how she would tell Jean. She would ask if Barrie was with her, and was she sitting down? She would explain the diagnosis, but then reassure her that in two week's time Margaret would be undergoing surgery.

At seven o'clock that night Carole picked up the telephone. Everything went to plan until Jean's voice croaked with tears. Carole's eyes moistened once again, but after a few moments, calmness was restored.

"I think I'll try to come up to Burnley," said Jean. "I'll ring Margaret, but not tonight, maybe in a couple of days."

Carole said goodbye to Jean and hopelessly wished there wasn't so many miles between them. The downside of the telephone was not being able to share hugs in desperate times.

The weekend following the telephone call, Jean was out in Poole shopping with her daughter, Claire. The precinct was a fleet of small shops. A florists, a trendy beauty parlour, a French patisserie, a small boutique selling ultra modern swimwear, and many more tiny retail buildings, stood proud like a flotilla anchored in the harbour.

"Oh, let's go in here mum," beamed Claire, "look at those soft teddies." Claire was in before her mum had time to blink.

The shop was a treasure-trove of collectibles. Cards for all occasions were everywhere. Instantly Jean spotted a card and thought of Margaret, "To my friend, thinking of you," it read.

"I'll buy that," thought Jean aloud, "I can't read the verse now though, or I'll be in tears."

She kept her thoughts to herself, but whilst Claire was 'oohing and ahhing' over the cuddly toys, Jean was gathering tiny presents to put in the post and send to her friend up North.

Chapter Twenty-Nine

By the third week in April 2002, Christine had at long last received the okay for surgery now that her blood pressure was stable. The timing was perfect for the family because it meant that the worst part would be over in time to celebrate Lucy's 21st birthday. Lucy had decided that she would have an open-house party from 4:00 p.m. for family and friends, then later in the evening the younger ones would go clubbing and continue the celebrations until the early hours. Things did not go to plan.

Christine only stayed in hospital overnight as she had a high temperature, and the anaesthetist declared her unfit for surgery. Her Consultant came to talk to her to say she would have some antibiotics, stay away from work, and then he could reschedule her op for May 9^{th,} which was two days before Lucy's birthday. Christine wouldn't even be at home to quietly celebrate with her family. She was upset, but Lucy was devastated, even at twenty-one years of age she still could not understand that some things don't always go to plan.

To try and make it up to Lucy, Christine and Peter decided to buy a kitten as a surprise for her. The family's pet, and almost family member, Bob, had died just before Christmas at the age of fourteen years. Owing to rules and regulations at the RSPCA, pets could not be taken until all the family had been introduced to the animal. And so it was that Peter, Christine and Lucy wandered around looking for the right kitten. They were all allocated to someone, and so it was arranged that the following morning they would meet Sally, a work colleague of Lucy's in Darwen, and take one of her cat's litter.

Just coincidentally, it was a tiny ginger tom, not unlike Bob. Armed with a giant-sized cat basket they went to their rendezvous. It was difficult at first glimpse to see a kitten at all, for under Sally's cardigan there seemed to be little more than a tiny ball of fluff. The six-month old kitten turned out to be just six weeks! He travelled home, not in the basket, but in the palm of Christine's hand, then he was warmly tucked inside her jumper, at the same time making tiny whimpering noises.

First stop was the pet shop for some kitten formula milk. Alfie, as he became christened, is now a fully fledged member of the Thornton family, and thoroughly spoilt rotten!

Again the day arrived and Christine had her hysterectomy, it nearly didn't happen because her blood count was below six, which increased the risk associated with anaesthetic. The nurse took Christine down to theatre and said that the anaesthetist wanted to speak to her again. Here she highlighted further the risks involved, but said that her Consultant felt that the blood count would continue to drop if she did not have the surgery.

Christine agreed and asked, "Will you watch over me very carefully?"

"Of course, my dear," said the anaesthetist.

"Then wheel me in," she demanded.

Peter waited anxiously for Christine to be brought back from the theatre, but was a little shocked when he saw his wife with oxygen mask, drip stands with fluids, and a machine attached to her that was giving her morphine for pain relief, together with a drain, filling with bright red blood, which appeared to be coming out of her abdomen. Through blurred vision Christine could make out that Peter was there, then she indicated for him to leave as she was only half-conscious.

Things didn't improve as quickly as they should. Christine was not a good patient, because she was persistently vomiting, and so could not take in any oral fluids or light diet. All the gas inside her abdomen made her look nine month's pregnant. Visitors came and went, but she could not summon up any effort to make conversation, owing to her pain and sickness.

By Friday afternoon she had not shown much sign of improvement at all, and when the physiotherapist came to see her and help her to find a comfortable position, the coughing up of blood started. Christine knew the implications of this was a pulmonary embolism. The Consultant was called in, and injections commenced, strict bed-rest, and x-rays and such were ordered for after the weekend.

Saturday morning showed a surprise visit from two dear friends, Moi and Irene. Christine and Moi always ribbed each other, but she could not even be bothered to banter with him about how he just knew that she would have a private room with a carpet, no less; whilst Irene who had recently been in hospital herself, had been on a busy ward with a lot of old dears. Still being sick Christine waved them off.

Carole had informed Margaret and Kath that she did not look too good. They came armed with the most exotic flowers. This was due to Margaret once having told the girls at Kathleen's shop to supply 'only the best for her friends'.

Margaret's first words as they entered Christine's room, just as she was yet again wretching more of the horrible yellow bile stuff, and trying not to cough, whilst holding onto her wounded abdomen was, "What the bloody hell have they done to you?"

Kath, ever the nurse, just held her vomit bowls and exchanged them for clean ones. Margaret held onto and squeezed her hand. Christine was aware her friends were with her as she drifted in and out of sleep; she didn't remember them leaving but the floral arrangement confirmed that they had been.

It was the following Tuesday before she felt like opening the mountain of cards and gifts. There were many good wishes from people she knew, and family of course, but the most poignant message brought tears. It was a card from Margaret, with such beautiful words about friendship on the card complete with four tiny candles.

The message from Margaret just read, "Get better soon, I need you."

These words made Christine reflect over parts of her life, and what her priorities had been. Work achievements rated pretty high, of course her family was the most important, as too were special friends, all knowing who they are. But altogether it made her appreciate how lucky she was with her lot. Life had been a struggle at times during the early years which she and Peter shared, but they had done a good job with all three of their children. They both loved and respected each other. They had become soul mates.

Justin was happily married to Amanda. Alex had just recently met Maria, who appeared to be the right girl to settle Alex down, and Lucy was young, healthy and happy.

Christine decided there and then that work would take a back seat, and family and friends would always come first and foremost. She would get better, she knew that, and looked forward to being at home, and as she convalesced she would care and be there for her friend Margaret.

Chapter Thirty

Sunless skies predicted moody shadows all summer long. The dismal climate loitered during the coming weeks and months, leaving the five pals plunged into a sullen decline, especially with the onset of Margaret's devastating news. It was as though an invisible person had control of a dimmer switch taking away their brightness. Now and then, the switch seemed turned up enough to reveal narrow beams of light, but the girls felt no trace of warmth from this source. What they did discover was a new-found closeness. It was a closeness that ran much deeper and stronger than ever before. They were a ring of protection, shielding, defending, and guarding over each other, with Margaret appearing to be the strongest of them all. This never ending circle of friends generated so much warmth.

The weeks passed with spanking speed. Frustratingly Margaret was enduring lots of essential procedures, in a process of elimination, to rule out further spread of the disease. Treatment seemed a long time in coming for everyone. The good thing from this lot of tests revealed that Margaret's lungs were clear from the offending tumour. The bad thing was that the Consultant Surgeon was now on holiday for two weeks, so it would be May before her appointment. What must have been the most devastating news for Margaret and Colin when they did see the surgeon, was to be told that the tumour would be inoperable, owing to the position in which it was placed. The alternative given was for Margaret to undergo radium treatment at the Christie Hospital, Manchester. He also thought that her liver might possibly be involved, and that once at Christie's, a more thorough test would confirm or deny this.

The weeks were moving fast, May was seeing the beginning of June on her shoulders, and Margaret had not yet begun her treatment. Jean did manage to make an early trip to Burnley that year, as she felt that she needed to be near her friend, to give her support, and so the usual get-together took place. It was to be a short visit, but it would of course include a trip to see Mrs. Hand. Jean felt lucky that she managed to spend some quality time with Margaret on her own, knowing that this would be the healthiest that she would see her friend. They talked privately. Jean was coming to terms herself with illness, she had the start of cancerous cells, and because she was having treatment which would more or less prevent any further damage to her tissues, it enabled her to cope.

Margaret's illness diverted Jean's mind away from her own troubles. Knowing that Margaret did not have the same chance as she did, upset her greatly. Life was not fair, she kept telling herself. Jean felt very positive about her own diagnosis, but she felt that she could not share this with her friends, as it would be like a slap in the face for Margaret. When the girls were altogether though, it was only Margaret who did not appear subdued, and the effect made the others snap out of their gloom. Jean returned to her home, promising that she would be back in August, as usual!

Margaret now openly talked about her illness and forthcoming treatment. In fact, she had decided that if she lost her hair through the invasive drug therapy, then she would get a posh wig from a quality shop in Blackpool. Apparently this shop was recommended by Christie's themselves in their booklet. It would be an auburn straight-cut, shoulder-length bob style.

There was always someone in Margaret's house when any of the girls called, always someone keeping her company, and keeping her mind occupied. Christine's job was checking the prescription; it seemed Margaret trusted nobody, owing to her morphine being under-prescribed on one occasion. She valued Christine's expertise, and had her working dosages out.

Once it was declared correct, Margaret would smile, as if to say, "I'll take it now!"

Life carried on as normal for Margaret and Colin to the outside world. What they said and felt behind closed doors was for them and the four walls only. She still went on the lane for her groceries, bartering with Khalid from the Spar, trying to get cheaper coke for her whisky of course. Debates would take place with Keith at the butchers over the best barbecued roast chicken, and she was never far away from her friend Kathleen Lord, putting her two pen'orth in with any customers who were around. Colin's tea was still ready, Shelby, Ian and the three grandchildren would still come for tea on Friday, with Thursdays being reserved for Nick and Ryan. So nothing changed there.

Margaret continued going to her mother's, the only difference being that one of the girls would collect her, so that she did not get too tired struggling up the brow at the top of Harold Street. This was a real bonus for Mrs. Hand, because she saw one of her other 'daughters' at the same time.

Whilst Margaret was awaiting assessment for Christie hospital, Carole and Alan went on holiday touring France and Spain in their camper-van. It was a guilt-ridden trip, but had been planned since February. The culpability was spineless actually, as both had worked tirelessly and were relying on a break to prepare them for the rough road ahead. Carole kept in touch with Christine whilst travelling. There was some concern about the cancer spreading to Margaret's liver, and she wanted to know as soon as possible the outcome of this. During a phone call to Christine from deep in the Pyrenees, Carole was told that the outlook appeared brighter, as no other organs had been affected. Margaret would start treatment in July. Carole and Alan had arranged to sail home from Cherbourg to Poole, which was a convenient place to meet up with Jean.

From the ferry Carole could identify the West Wight Downs of the Isle of Wight, and the isolated white rock stacks known as the Needles, stretching out into the Solent. Then they viewed the suburbs of Bournemouth and beyond as they sailed into Poole Harbour. The enormous natural harbour threw out an emotional liferaft for Carole, she really needed to step on dry land to see Jean once again.

Once they docked, the mobile phones were especially useful. After much back-tracking and riding around in circles they found Jean at a family pub. After kissing and hugging they got down to business and talked of Margaret's illness. Jean gave a huge sigh of relief at the absence of the dreaded disease in other organs.

Carole lightened the note, "She was really pleased with your present Jean. She said that you had sent her a lucky bag, with bits of all sorts in it."

"Yeh," Jean said in her now Dorset accent. "Some of the words on the card and the fridge magnet were lovely, but they don't half bring a lump to your throat."

"She's using the sunflower key-ring," Carole assured her, "and the tiny card she keeps in her purse."

Before they knew it, it was time for Carole and Alan to leave Jean and travel up North to Burnley. They bid each other farewell once again.

"I'll keep in touch," promised Jean.

"Yes and you take care of yourself," said Carole, wrapping her arms around her friend, her eyes filling with tears so desperate to roll.

Both girls felt as though they were being punished for all the good times they had shared, as if it was now pay-back time.

Carole was passing her spare time hand-making a huge leopard-skin blanket for Margaret to snuggle up to on the days she felt cold and tired. Margaret loved anything with fake leopard-skin. Radium therapy in its fight to save life, also had the power to destroy vitality.

July 7th, Margaret's forty-ninth birthday was fast approaching. Her friends bought her presents as appropriate as possible. Kath had found a hand-painted water jug and drinking glass, embroidered in lavender, and also lilac candles packed in an embossed silver tube, and a lilac throw over for her bed. Christine bought a beautiful lemon nightdress and dressing-gown, to finish her hospital trousseau.

Margaret's living-room was always scented with exotic flowers, for her friends from Kathleen's florist never failed to ensure that she had a welcome supply.

At least one day a week Christine would take Margaret out, usually browsing at one of the mill shops, where they would have coffee and cake. Egg custard or a vanilla slice were favourites, because Margaret could eat all the filling. She developed a craving for the vanilla. They agreed that the best ever was made at the BSK bakery where Pat used to work years before, when she used to bring the damaged ones home for the girls. Nothing tasted quite so good nowadays, so Christine asked Justin, who was a chef, if he could make Margaret some vanilla? He was honoured to be able to do something to help, and it was delicious. He made plenty, enough for Margaret to store some in her freezer.

Whilst on their travels, Margaret would buy any artefacts which would enhance her bedroom, as she was having it decorated in lilac and white. The main item on the agenda during these trips, was of course bedroom furniture. She wanted antique pine, to go with the king-size bed which had been ordered. At last they found two wardrobes, a large chest of drawers, a bedding box and two bedside tables, which were ordered especially to her own design. The bedroom was to be decorated whilst Margaret was in hospital, so any effects of dust and paint did not affect her chest, causing her any further discomfort.

Fun still reigned on these outings, in particular when they shopped for food at the local supermarket. Margaret stocked up on all Colin's favourite foods, tins of meat, pizzas, and meals for one. Kath once joined them after work; it was hard to remember just what made them laugh so much that they cried, but to the onlooker, they resembled two people who required a nurse to chaperone them.

Week after week the supermarket became attached to the trip to the mill shop. Christine felt sure that Margaret was ensuring that Colin would never need to food shop again! He would be already home when they arrived with the bulging bags of groceries, and so he would be full of glee as Margaret showed him their wares.

He showed enthusiasm as he would ask, "Well girls, where have you been today, and what have you bought besides groceries?"

"Oh this and that, presents for Xmas and such, nothing to concern yourself with," Margaret would inform him.

He was pleased that she was not just sitting around the house, he never said, but it was felt that he was so grateful to Margaret's friends supporting, and most of all caring for his wife, while he tried to maintain a degree of normality.

Margaret tried to share her time between all her friends; she would go to different places with each of them. In her mind's eye, she used each one of them to buy each other's Xmas and birthday presents, just in case she did not feel up to shopping once she had completed her treatment. Each one of them knew what Margaret had bought for the others. She tried not to leave anyone out of her time.

The occasional Saturday morning was spent with Anne, usually shopping for food, yet again, and finishing with coffee and a natter. Margaret had first met Anne Wilson in the maternity hospital, where they both gave birth to sons, so they had known one another for a long time. Some years after the birth of her son, Anne had given birth to a daughter Caroline, who had grown to look upon Margaret as a cherished Aunty.

On Sundays if Margaret felt up to a run out, she and Colin would go for a meal with Kathleen and Michael Lord, not managing this every week, but nevertheless when they did go they all had a good time, trying not to discuss illness of any kind.

Both Christine and Carole had been thinking the same thing, and that was that Father Fraher should know about Margaret, they felt that he would want to be kept informed. He still went regularly to visit Mrs. Hand, and she may well need to confide in him. So it was after the evening mass on Saturday that they went to speak to him.

Shocked and worried he told the girls that he would call to see Margaret. He wasted no time, for he called two days later. Neither girl told Margaret that they had spoken to Father Fraher.

It was in fact Margaret herself who mentioned it, "Guess who came to see me today?"

Before they could try to guess, she said, "Father Fraher, I think that my mother must have told him I was ill. Anyway, I feel so much better, quite relieved actually, I feel that I have made my peace with God. It helps you know. He said that he would call again, too."

"Good I'm glad," each girl answered.

One person who Margaret did confide in was Kathleen Lord's son, Anthony. He worked as a nurse in palliative care, and although Margaret wasn't one of his patients he found time to call and talk to her. Margaret never once cried in front of her friends, she knew it would be too raw for all of them, herself included. But one time she did cry with Anthony. She must have felt safe with him, while he held nothing but respect and friendship for her.

Chapter Thirty-One

Two options were offered to Margaret on admission to the famous Christie Hospital. She could travel the thirty miles daily, or receive residential medical care. Nursing professionals advised the latter, as the ferocious radiotherapy treatment often drained patients of all their energy. She didn't appear anxious at all, in fact she bought a new suitcase and packed it meticulously with night wear, day wear and the recommended toiletries, as though she was going on her holidays. Never one to admit fear, Margaret faced this episode of her life with great courage, seeing a further chance to show her metal.

As Colin didn't drive, all his and Margaret's friends wanted to ensure he could visit her whenever he liked. Everyone came to the conclusion that Christine, though still convalescing from her own illness, should hold a list of people's telephone numbers, thereby setting up a rota of volunteer drivers. An abundance of people were willing to enrol on the list. Some had to forfeit extra visits so as not to tire Margaret too much.

Carole and Alan drove Colin down the M60 the first evening. Unexpectedly the sun was shining. They picked Colin up from home around 4:15 p.m.

They found him to be very chatty. "You know we said we'd decorate the bedroom whilst she's away?"

"Yeh," Carole answered.

"Well we've started, and the bloody ceiling has fallen down! We'll have to work like the clappers to get it finished. Ryan was just ready to paint, so he's as sick as a chip."

"Do you think you'll have it finished?" asked Carole.

"There's no think about it," laughed Colin. "She'll go mad if it's not. Have you seen what she's bought? All new furniture, bedding, curtains, and carpeting. All the old stuff has gone. You wouldn't believe the stuff she's hoarded over the years. Anyway we'll have to have a fresh start now because it's all been dumped."

The conversation progressed from one thing to another. Alan had momentarily lost his concentration, so they were truly lost, riding around Didsbury, Altrincham and Cheadle. The little map they'd been given didn't make much sense to them. Eventually, half an hour later than planned, they drove past Margaret, who was sucking on a delicious, soothing ice lolly, sitting in the gardens of the hospital.

As they parked the little green car (their ever faithful transport), Alan looked around, and in a complimentary fashion said, "Isn't this a marvellous place?"

"Never wanted to visit anybody in this place!" Colin commented in a cold piercing tone.

His message rang home loud and clear. He was right, they were beggared to reason why they were there?

They were all silent as Colin carried the huge hand-tied bouquet to the gardens of the main entrance, where his wife was sitting.

"I nearly gave you up," said Margaret teasingly.

"It was our fault Margaret; we got lost," apologised Carole.

"Come on let's put these flowers away, and I'll show you my living quarters."

Margaret gave a grand tour of the wonderfully maintained establishment. She was allowed to use her time freely, so they ate tea at the hospital's local pub just a few yards round the corner. At nine o'clock Carole and Alan made their way back to the car, whilst Colin walked Margaret back to the small dormitory that she shared with three other women.

It was difficult to accept the gravity of her illness. She had looked dazzlingly trendy in her denim jacket and matching skirt, fashion items that she wasn't able to wear before her weight loss. Her elegant slip-on shoes, painted toenails and designer sunshades, added up to a glamorous façade, which had almost encroached on the pretty surrounding cultivation.

As friends and family queued in turn to visit this cheerful and forthright lady, people admired, and even envied her virtue. There was nothing flimsy about her personality, just plucky and spirited. She met other patients sharing the same plight, realising that this illness attacked people from all walks of life and of any age. She actively listened to their life stories with eager curiosity and sensitivity. This was the positive side of Margaret's hospital experience. She spoke with sympathetic reverence of a lady who lived over one hundred miles away; her family not owning a car, meant that she rarely had visitors.

One evening Margaret said to Carole, "Tell Christine it doesn't matter about someone coming every day, I'll spend some time with Mary, she's often on her own." This was typical of Margaret. She rang her mum each night offering reassurance of her well-being. Mrs. Hand fought the brave fight with her daughter by means of ...was it denial or was it acceptance?

Kathleen and Michael Lord visited one Sunday and took Margaret to the Trafford Centre. Friends rallied round to ensure that Margaret, Rita and Shirley managed to visit their friend. Kath went along too.

One afternoon following their shift at Burnley, Carole gave Kath a lift home. It was at this time that Kath confided of her regretful visit.

"Oh Carole," she said with a ripening red face. "It brought back so many sad memories, the last time I went there was Christmas Day, I was only eleven. From that day I knew that my mum was going to die. It's haunting me. I didn't think I would be reliving this with my friend Margaret, I just wanted to pick her up and run away. Why does life have to be so unfair and so cruel!"

"I don't know Kath, I wish I had a magic wand to rid everyone of all their hurt," said Carole slowly and dejectedly.

The Thursday before Margaret's homecoming Carole, Christine and Kathleen from the florist, with Colin's permission, set out the beautifully decorated bedroom, whilst Kath kept Mrs. Hand company. Lilac and silver bedside lamps were put in place, and cream voile curtains flowed in the evening breeze. Crisp new bed linen dressed the new bed, whilst lilac candles and trinkets made the room appear as inviting as a five-star hotel, or a French lady's boudoir. This was indeed a place where Margaret could relax and rest, once she arrived home after her arduous radium treatment.

Chapter Thirty-Two

Margaret made a pact between herself and her illness, a treaty in secret, like a weapon to protect her eighty-five year old mother. One night, whilst alone with Mrs. Hand, before any of the girls arrived, Margaret expressed her wishes. She spoke to her mother in such a matter-of-fact way, that she may just as well have been giving her a shopping list. This was Margaret's last visit to see her mother, as from then on all catching up on daily events was carried out by telephone.

Of course the girls kept up their visits, they became the buffer for Mrs. Hand's emotional turmoil as they shared together their hopes, fears and anxieties. *'Let's just take one day at a time'* became their motto.

As Mrs. Hand bolted the doors behind them following their visits, she never failed to say, "I don't know what I would do without you girls, I've always said that I've got five daughters."

The compliment was always returned by, "And what would we do without you, Mrs. Hand? You've always been there for us."

Lots of people became sensitive to the old lady's plight, realising that she must be missing her daughter's visits. They would offer half an hour out of their own time, to shorten Mrs. Hand's day. Pam, her home-help, took her role beyond the course of duty and stayed many an afternoon to keep her company.

Christine telephoned Margaret, there was nothing unusual about that, but she said that she was going to Blackburn shopping. However she would not take Margaret with her because she was starting with a cold and it was a miserable wet day; she did ask if there was anything she needed?

The reply on the phone sounded as if someone was very upset and extremely disappointed. "I want to come with you, Christine, I've been looking forward to going out."

Margaret now attended relaxation classes and massage at Rossendale hospital. She was picked up on Thursday morning and brought back at one o'clock, so the day for the outings was changed to Wednesdays. Thursday afternoon left Margaret sleepy, she enjoyed and benefited from the treatment, but she was very tired following it, and could be seen cuddled up with her blanket which Carole had patiently and lovingly made for her. Whilst there, she never missed the opportunity of being nosy, for always she had to know about other people, she always acquired some gems of information which she would share with her friends, knowing that they did not know the person in question, and that she wasn't breaking any confidences.

"Margaret, you shouldn't go out, if you've got a cold," Christine told her friend.

"Oh, please take me, I haven't been out all week and I'm sick of these four walls."

"All right, but you must get wrapped up, I mean it, put your long mac on, and something on your head, and wear your gloves. Promise me!"

Christine knew that she sounded like a mother trying to protect her young child from the elements, but off they went for some Xmas shopping, which was always a bit more exciting than food. And although they did not stay very long, Margaret did seem to be a little bit revived from the fresh air.

The dark dismal days of November arrived, bringing with them an almighty shock. Wet and blustery, the skies held no light, providing little daylight, ensuring that the mood of the people was low. Ironically Kath did escape the fuss and celebrations of her 50th birthday, the day came and went with a low profile. Presents and cards were exchanged, but Kath was secretly pleased with all this. Of course the weekend to Stratford had been put on hold, although the girls would enjoy their little holiday eventually. For now at least, the time was not right, and when Margaret felt able they would go then.

Chapter Thirty-Three

Christine was now back at work, she was gradually using her holidays up, and so not yet working a full week. It was Monday morning when she received the telephone call from Kath.

Sounding desperate and worried, Kath relayed to Christine the events of the morning. Kath was on annual leave for a week, so she rang Margaret to see if she wanted anything bringing back from town, and to let her know that she would come to her house when she had finished her errands. It was Colin who answered the phone, and Kath's heart sank at hearing his voice. She realised that Margaret must be ill for Colin not to be at work. He informed Kath that the doctor was there and he was thinking of admitting Margaret to hospital and asked Kath to call him back in fifteen minutes.

Feeling alone and unsure of what to do she telephoned Christine, for all Kath could think about was that she did not know where she would be admitted to? Christine reassured her saying that she would find out through the switchboard, and that she should get herself up to the ward as Carole was on duty, and Kath should not be on her own.

Ward 24 was the place where Margaret was taken, and once Kath had calmed down, Christine told her and Carole to go together to see their friend. Although Margaret was having oxygen therapy, and appeared breathless and anxious, they both felt that once she received antibiotics she would be on the mend and ready to return home. They convinced themselves that it was the cold which was the problem, and not her illness. They came back to the unit looking relieved and happier, so they all had a cup of tea and a chat about Margaret, and it was agreed that Christine would visit later that evening before she finished her shift.

Christine made her way to Ward 24, not hurrying or rushing as she had learnt from Kath and Carole that the admission seemed to be on the side of caution rather than necessity. The curtain was drawn around the bed, she could hear the familiar voices of Colin and Margaret and an unfamiliar voice, which evidently belonged to the nurse. Margaret was being assisted out of bed to go to the toilet. A wobbly drip stand was used as a crutch for her to support herself, whilst her other arm was interlinked with the nurse.

Either she had deteriorated during the afternoon, or her friends had misjudged her condition. With an unsteady gait and gasping for breath, Margaret spotted Christine; those beautiful deep brown eyes, now relayed fear, like that of a startled animal.

She spluttered out to the nurse, "My friend's here now, she'll take me to the toilet."

Whilst the nurse was getting ready to protest, Christine gestured to her that she would be glad to help her friend.

Colin helped Christine settle Margaret back into bed. She was cold and clammy, so she washed her hands and face and brushed her long hair, arranging it neatly into a black velvet scrunchie. All their family had now gathered, so Christine took this as her cue to leave. She kissed Margaret goodnight assuring her that she would see her the following day, at the same time letting Colin know that he could ring her anytime if he needed anything.

She had intended to go straight home, but she could not go to her car just yet, instead she found herself returning to her place of work. In times of distress or upset, the unit beckons its staff, as there is guaranteed support from colleagues. It felt like home at times like this. And so it was that Debbie, the Sister of the admissions unit, to whom Christine had spoken about her friend earlier in the day, offered Christine comfort in her time of need. After a few tears, she managed to compose herself enough to drive home, not wanting to take in what she had seen in Margaret.

The highlight of the week for the sisters and their husbands was taking part in the local pub-quiz. It was taken very seriously, for they all liked to win. Normally this night was full of fun and laughter, but tonight the atmosphere was heavy.

"I think that you're wrong Carole about Margaret, I've just been to see her, she looks dreadful. She won't get better with antibiotics, I think it is the cancer," Christine angrily told her sister.

Margaret 'Scanny' just said knowingly, "That's just how Norman was."

Empathy was shown by Margaret and Mick Scanlon, their team-mates and friends, who were also friends of Margaret and Colin. They were dragging themselves through the early stages of the grieving process over their dear brother, Norman. He was a truly talented local artist, and a great loss to the townsfolk and many friends, as well as his family. Uncannily, the big 'C' which had taken Norman, had reared its ugly head yet again. The close friends wept openly, without shame, whilst their menfolk looked on helplessly.

Thoughts of winning the quiz were no longer paramount, a good strong drink was what was needed, if only to help them sleep.

Chapter Thirty-Four

At 6:15 a.m. Carole dragged herself out of bed at a snail's pace. She hated dark mornings and often thought everyone should wake and sleep like the farmers – slumber when the sun goes down, and rise when the sun appears in the morning. But her work demanded early starts. Given a choice she would much prefer to loaf around tackling household chores in her own time. She hadn't slept well due to tossing and turning, worrying what sort of night Margaret had had?

One of her first thoughts was usually what time she would be climbing back into her bed that night? November 26th was different. After the ritual of shower, breakfast and packing up some lunch, Carole rang ward 24 and asked if they would mind if she called to see Margaret on her way to Deerplay Ward?

"Oh, just a minute," came the reply. "Margaret Fort has been moved to the Medical Assessment Centre, (MAC). It seems that her condition is medical rather than surgical."

Carole thanked the nurse for the information and felt a slight sense of relief.

"It's just a chest infection," she reasoned with herself.

By 6:45 a.m. Carole found herself on MAC. She hadn't bothered to ring for permission to visit because patients and relatives are brought onto that ward at all times day and night.

The ward was hushed and dimmed. After approaching a nurse carrying an armful of white starched sheets she said, "Good morning. I work here at the hospital and I just wondered if you would mind if I said 'hello' to Margaret - Margaret Fort?"

"Are you a relative?" asked the nurse.

"No, but I'm a really good friend, she won't mind."

"But will you be all right on your own she's quite poorly. I've rung her husband but I don't think he has taken on board what I've said." The nurse's eyes expressed sympathy which alarmed Carole.

"I think I'll be okay," she said with a half-hearted smile.

Margaret's bed was shielded by the flowered curtains. Stepping through the opening, Carole was aghast at the sight before her. No matter what words the nurse had used, nothing could have prepared her for this moment. She knelt at the side of the bed, crouching close to her friend who was lying half on her front and half on her side. She was unpleasantly warm and clammy; her hair felt damp.

"Margaret, Margaret," Carole repeated in a whisper. "It's me, Carole." She paused before continuing, "I'm not going to leave you, but I'm ringing for Colin, I won't be long. Is that all right?"

Margaret spoke very slowly as she squeezed her pal's hand, "Yeh, it's alright, Carole."

She came from behind the curtains where the nurse was waiting, not at all surprised by Carole's silent weeping. "I must ring Colin, he's needed here, isn't he?"

"Yes of course," said the nurse, touching Carole's arm. "Like I said I have rung him, but I'm not sure he understood what I was trying to tell him."

"Better still," Carole continued, "I'll ring my sister, she's a nurse and Colin doesn't drive, he might be waiting for a taxi. It'll take ages. Christine will bring him."

After making the urgent phone call, and gaining the knowledge that Christine would bring Colin, Carole went back to the bedside of her friend. She sat holding and stroking Margaret, trying to comfort her. She prayed and beseeched that her laboured breathing would hold out until Christine arrived with Colin.

Peter was quietly getting ready for work, creeping around, trying not to waken his wife, he was aware that she had slept very little, tossing and turning for most of the night. But Christine was watching his every move, when the telephone rang, it jolted her out of bed. It was Carole, urgently telling her to get hold of Colin and get themselves up to MAC as soon as possible. Nervously, she telephoned him. His line was engaged, he was getting the same tone, as he was ringing Christine, taking her up on her offer of a lift.

Colin got in the car, not giving much away with his facial expression. Christine put a hand on his and told him to expect the worst. Although it was still dark, there were plenty of people milling around. Colne Road was busy with people walking, cycling, and driving to work. Christine wished at this moment that she too was on her way to work, her nerves felt raw and fragile.

After a poor night she had some difficulty steering her concentration. "Get your professional hat on and focus on Margaret's family, who need you right now," she scolded herself. Her thoughts untangling the puzzle in her head, she took a deep breath allowing her mind to clear.

They were met by an anxious Carole who escorted them both to Margaret. Hers was the only bed with the curtains drawn, to try and give some privacy. There was very little noise on the ward, the day shift had not yet arrived, and the nurses were quietly writing up their night reports. Only the odd muffled sound from the other patients who seemed to sense the need for quietness could be heard. The sound from shoes echoed loudly, and unconsciously the three of them tried to silence them with creeping footsteps.

Then it didn't matter about being quiet, for the heart-rending sob which Colin gasped could be heard everywhere. It was so powerful, so painful to the listener, that it made Christine and Carole just cover their mouths with their hands, so that their own sobs were silenced. Their tears freely fell as they left Colin alone with his beloved.

Kath was not in when Carole first called, which left her frantic. Christine calmed her down, reassuring her that they would find her sooner or later. It was as though whatever happened now, they all needed to be together. They had ridden this rough road together, all carried the load clinging together, their nerves too, were beginning to feel frazzled and charred. Christine ordered Carole up to Deerplay Ward for ten minutes, where she would be met with warmth and understanding. Some of the friends on the ward had followed the sequence of Margaret's illness, listening attentively.

The Children's Unit at Burnley General had lost an admirable colleague, Denise, at a shockingly young age to a similar illness. People were still in mourning, especially the auxiliary nurses who had worked so closely with her. After drinking a soothing beaker of tea, Carole was dismissed to be with her friend during her last hours. During this time Christine managed to contact Kath, who assured her that she was on her way.

MAC has some provision for relatives, albeit not very private, but it is greatly appreciated by all who use it. Colin gave Christine the list which Margaret had previously compiled, with all the important telephone numbers on. She took on the responsibility of contacting immediate family, namely Ryan, Margaret's son, also Shelby and Nick her stepchildren, whom she cared for so dearly.

Catching Margaret's children in was a struggle initially, because they were busy getting their own children ready for school, and she was glad once this task was over. Colin needed his family by his side. Barbara, his sister, was someone he wanted to help him get through the rough time ahead.

Very soon everyone who needed to be there arrived. The doctor, who had been on duty throughout the night, came to talk to Colin, to prepare him. Christine asked Colin if he wanted her to go with him to the relatives room? He did, so she witnessed the doctor gently tell

Colin that they had tried everything they could to help Margaret, but it seemed that it was the cancer which had taken hold of her body. He could only tell Colin that her death was imminent. Colin already knew this from just seeing her. As they came out of the room, Christine asked Colin if they could let Father Fraher know?

"Yes, I forgot about him, you'd better ring him," he answered. It was as though he had a list in his mind of what he had to do when the time came.

During this time the staff had unobtrusively moved Margaret into a single room situated at the bottom of the ward, giving the family a place of privacy, where they could express their grief.

Kath arrived looking pale and shocked. All the children gradually arrived and one of the girls showed them where their mother was.

The friends stayed quietly in the waiting area at the top of the ward, ready for when they could say their goodbyes to their friend, but trying not to be intrusive. The nurses were wonderful, insisting that they use the office telephone to call whoever they needed to. Carole managed to speak to Jean, who was too upset to talk, so she told her she would call back later in the day.

"Father Fraher, it's Carole Hawke, er em, Trickett."

After a difficult pause, the name registered with the priest. The same priest who had watched these girls grow up, marry and have babies, and now they were old enough to be grandparents.

"Yes, Carole," he spoke in his fluent Irish lilt. "What can I do for you dear?"

"It's Margaret, Father, she's really ill in hospital. I think this is it, can you come?"

"I'm just about to go into church and say Mass, Carole. Can I ring my mate, Father Jennings, oh he's good, he'll look after Margaret." Father Fraher's speech and manner were as broad as his congregation's.

"Yes, of course you can Father, she's on the Medical Assessment Centre, next to the chapel. Will you offer your Mass up for her?"

"Sure, yeh, what about her mum, does she know how poorly Margaret is?" he asked.

"I think Ryan has gone to tell her, I'm going now Father, I'll keep in touch."

"Yes, do now, God bless."

Father Fraher's voice had become throatier over the years, but Carole knew that he'd understood the gravity of the situation.

Carole did call Jean again, who expressed her need to keep in touch.

"I'll be with you all every step of the way," she'd said. Jean didn't know whether she herself would actually be able to face up to this situation in person, but on the other hand she wanted to drop everything to be amongst her friends and say goodbye to her soul mate, Margaret. She was in such a dilemma.

Carole couldn't help, because none of the girls knew what was in store, all she could do was to promise to ring her if there was any change.

Within twenty minutes Father Fraher's Irish colleague dressed in his black attire, appeared quietly and discreetly. To his right, sat in a small dimmed alcove were three women. Unmistakably he knew that these ladies with faces as deep as spate, had to be the girls on whose behalf Father Fraher had telephoned.

"Am I right? You must be the friends of Margaret," he seemed to speak harmoniously. "I'm Father Jennings, the hospital chaplain."

He held out a warm hand to each of them as they introduced themselves in turn.

"I believe, she's very ill, your friend Margaret."

"Yes Father, she is," they answered in a low chorus.

"Well now if you just lead me to where Margaret is, I'll give her God's blessing and say a few little prayers."

Christine showed him the room, right at the end of the long Nightingale Ward.

After a short time he met the girls on his way back. He paused and turned. In the half-light Father Jenning's shadowed face appeared vexed. Maybe at the sight of life fading, and a family in agonising grief, he could offer little comfort. As hospital chaplain this was one of his most perplexing duties, yet he had the privilege of giving sanctifying grace.

A few moments later, with his hands clasped, he said, "You know Father Fraher has told me quite a lot about you girls, how you all grew up together, and went to his youth club." He raised his voice in good humour.

"Yes, Father," agreed Christine. "We all went, we had a right good time."

"I'm sure you did, my dear, as did Father Fraher!" Father Jennings laughed, and lifted his eyebrows teasingly. "Now then, he tells me that you all work here, shouldn't you be at work now?"

"Well," Christine explained, "we all work on the Paediatric Unit. Kath is on holiday, I'm on a day off, and Carole should be there, but they've been very understanding and don't mind her being here."

"Well that's helpful, so it is. I'm sure that you all do marvellous jobs there. I'll be off now, but I'll be praying for Margaret and you girls. Let me know if there's any change."

"Yes Father," rang out three voices of obedience. "Thank you Father, thanks for everything."

As the priest left, the girls felt a tinge of relief knowing that Margaret had received the sacrament of Extreme Unction – the last rites.

In the middle of the morning, Kathleen came up, abandoning her shop to the care of her staff. Feeling distressed she sat with the girls.

Joan, Kath's sister, worked on a ward near MAC, and came to offer comfort to all the girls and to say her 'goodbye' to Margaret. Joan made tea and toast for all of them, feeling at least she was doing something to help. Ryan had informed his grandma that Margaret was in hospital.

Carole thought it best to go and sit with Mrs. Hand for an hour. Kathleen Lord had arranged to take Rita later that afternoon to spend some time with her. Carole made her way to Mrs. Hand's knowing they would share their pain together. As she put her head around the living-room door she found her sat silently, filled with her own thoughts.

"Oh come in love, our Ryan's rung, how is she love?" came the quiet questioning voice.

"Not so good, Mrs. Hand," Carole answered, holding the old lady's hand, whilst kneeling beside her.

"Do you think this is it? Is she going to die, love?"

"Well, she's really ill, we just have to let nature take its course Mrs. Hand, one day at a time."

"I know love, but I can't go up there. Ryan asked me if I wanted to go and see her? I can't Carole, I can't see her like that!"

"I know, I know, don't worry, Margaret wouldn't want you to either."

Both were crying, then sobbing.

"I'll tell you what, let's both have a drink of tea," suggested Carole. " I think that's what we need."

Just as the kettle boiled, Father Fraher knocked and walked in. He sat chatting of old times at the youth club, and of the time he accidentally set fire to Margaret's auburn hair. Conversation focused around Margaret and the present day.

Mrs. Hand referred to Leonard's philosophy of life, "Life is a length of string, where or when He cuts it, no one knows."

Chapter Thirty-Five

It was Colin who came for the girls, his gesture was more than they ever expected, because he was such a private person, they felt that he might struggle with their presence, and wish only to have his family around him. But no, as he spoke, he placed the palm of his hand on Christine's face saying, "Come on girls, you should be down there with Margaret."

Christine said, "We didn't want to intrude Colin, we knew you would let us say our goodbyes when you were ready, and besides all your family are there."

"You girls have more right to be there than some of them, you're her 'sisters'. In fact you're more than sisters, because you've never fallen out, and sisters often do."

He could not have paid them a higher compliment. They kissed him, then made their way to the room where Margaret slept fitfully.

The day was long and weary, tears flowed down anxious faces, sentimental words were uttered lovingly to this kind and wonderful person who was slowly ebbing away from life. Everyone who was at Margaret's bedside did not expect to see a new day dawn for her, whilst residing on MAC. Laboriously, Margaret expelled air, shallow breaths indicating that much effort was needed for her body to undertake this function, which would keep her alive. Bubbling noises sounded, filling her lungs with fluid, instead of circulating around her body to the important tissues to sustain life. She appeared to defy all the medics by still being with them.

At one point during the morning, she sat up in bed, she awoke with vengeance like that of a warrior, ready for battle. She amused all who were present, muttering words and short sentences, reliving the past.

"Rosemary Loftus, yes, umph," she quoted as she looked at Kath, obviously this message was for her to decipher.

Quite clearly she shouted of Alex. Was this something for Christine to be concerned about?

Sleeping again, but not for long as she sat upright and told Ryan, "White Roses, get white roses." Again, sleeping fitfully.

"They've always bin same!" she called out in her not so posh voice Awake yet again, eyebrows lifting with great expression.

It was as though she was sat in her own living-room, on her own settee, surrounded by her mates, reeling off the gossip which she'd picked up from the lane.

But there were tender moments too. Moments between mother and son. Ryan sat stroking Margaret's face slowly, whispering that she'd been his world over the years. Maternal love, love in its purest form, was fully respected by her loving son.

Colin, clasped his hands tightly around Margaret's, as his mind explored their twenty-years of marriage. She was his precious stone, a piece of amber, smooth and shiny, lovingly polished to a gloss. Exquisite shades of honey and vanilla, blonde mingling with deep chocolate, she was his treasure. Somehow he'd dreamt that he'd keep her forever.

Night-time was upon them yet again, all their children had decided to spend the night with Margaret and their father. Spread all over the floor and filling the chairs which had been brought in for them, they tried to sleep. The girls went to the visitor's room.

On hearing the sound of fast footsteps they went to meet the messenger.

"Christine, come quick," Shelby's expression was of excitement, she was half laughing.

Instantly Christine feared the time had come, but after seeing Shelby's face, thought maybe God had intervened by way of a miracle.

"She wants you to come and comb her hair, she just sat up in bed and said to go and fetch you, and then said to us, "You lot can go home, I can't sleep with you all staring at me!" Shelby informed the girls.

So off they trundled down to Margaret's room, to do her hair proud, where they stayed, watching their friend settle down to a more peaceful sleep, with Colin sleeping in the Parker Knoll easy chair, and her children now home to their beds.

With Wednesday came the rain and the howling wind, the windows in the room had been opened when the nurses came to wash and make Margaret more comfortable. This procedure worried everyone, because they thought that each movement would bring Margaret a step nearer to her death, for at times every breath she took sounded as though it could be her last.

The vertical blinds were closed to enhance peace in the room. It was 12:25 p.m. when a shaft of sunlight, (even though there was no evidence of any sunshine), appeared from a tiny gap in the blinds and stretched diagonally from the foot of the bed to the top of Margaret's face.

"Leonard," mouthed Christine, Kath and Carole, secretly.

They later discussed that they knew that Mr. Hand had come for his daughter, and that she would now go in peace. Carole felt that she had to go home for some sleep that night because by rights she had to work the following morning. And so it was that Kath, Christine and Colin spent the night with Margaret. It was ever so peaceful and quiet, with no one talking. Colin was asleep, but not soundly. How could he be? He must have been so very tired, just catnapping since Tuesday morning.

It was Christine who noticed the silvery lights, the raining of spiritual energy, not unlike a kaleidoscope, hovering towards Margaret and coming from nowhere. Trying to attract the attention of Kath, but not wanting to wake Colin, she managed to tell Kath that she could see something.

Kath crept from her chair and stood behind Christine, leaning across her shoulders, whispering that she too could see this vision, or was it an aura? They felt sure it was the angels coming to take Margaret's soul, just as when they were children and trusted in their Guardian

Angels to protect them whilst living here on earth. They believed Leonard, Margaret's father, would return amongst a throng of heavenly beings, and lift her soul to live forever with them. They drew much consolation from this, as they all believed in life after death. For Christine and Kath this dancing spiritual presence was a great source of comfort. To them this was the meaning of life, the end of a long pilgrimage, and the start of another great journey – a journey to peace with God.

It was Carole, who on her return said that there was something different about Margaret, following the bed-bath which the nurses had performed. And it was Christine who remarked that she looked both youthful and beautiful, because every line, every blemish of aged skin had now disappeared. Margaret was wearing the pale lemon nightdress which Christine had bought for her birthday. Her rich auburn hair was not in a bun, like she usually wore it, but in a pony-tail cascading around her shoulders. She looked stunning, as her full astonishing inner and outer beauty were revealed.

There was no way that Carole was going home that night, she too wanted to see if the spirits came again. They did! The room was black but for the moon flickering shadows, and the dim spotlight fixed in the ceiling high above the bed.

Christine thought that Carole had lost her marbles as she watched her wave her hands around, giving signs as though she was playing charades, but she was trying to attract her attention. She got up from her chair and went to see if her sister was all right.

Carole whispered that the spirits were here, and she could see them around the outline of Margaret's body.

"Don't be daft," snapped Christine, "I thought you'd gone barmy."

"But I **can** see them," insisted her sister. "It's like a rainbow of colours and mother of pearl all mixed into one," continued Carole.

Christine simply nodded in agreement.

In the hours that followed dawn, Carole was sure that Margaret's serenity which radiated round the room was the result of the spiritual happening.

Margaret's visitors came and went, some coping better than others at seeing this special person so ill. Philip came, he was extremely upset at the thought of losing Margaret. Daily functions had to be adhered to, like forcing meals down, in order to have the strength to stay for as long as it took.

On the way to the hospital restaurant, Philip spotted Dr. Kendra, whom he saw on a regular basis for his blood disorder. He entered the lift, where a bewildered Joan and Kath were entertained with Philip's antics.

"Do you know who I am, Dr. Kendra? asked Philip.

"Well, actually, I know that I see you. Ah yes, it's Mr. Trickett. I seem to remember that you cancelled your last appointment."

"Yes, I was poorly," commented Philip.

Dr. Kendra, pulled Philip's lower lids down on both eyes, and asked how he was now?

"Oh, I can't see you now, anyway, I'm visiting my friend, she's very ill, so I'll wait for my appointment," Philip answered.

It lightened the mood, as he explained to Joan that even if Dr. Kendra could see him, he wouldn't go. Dr.

Kendra must see hundreds of people constantly, but Philip felt that he was a personal friend of his!

Chapter Thirty-Six

One of Margaret's most distinguishing features were her beautifully manicured fingernails. If ever they were seen without polish they would always be buffered to a high gloss. Her toenails were treated to a pedicure periodically too. She had every reason to be proud of her hands and feet, but during the last few days, her nail varnish had chipped. Her fingers appeared to be changing colour, they were purple, and so the pale grey nail polish which covered them looked a mess.

This perturbed Colin somewhat. Rubbing his dark beard he said, "She'd go mad if she saw that," indicating the varnish peeling from her hands.

"You're right, she would Colin," said Christine. "We could do with a girlie night in, all we need is some nail varnish remover and some polish. She's got some moisturiser, which could be used for hand cream, and we could have a pamper night."

"What do you think Margaret?" they asked her; they had talked to Margaret throughout their time there.

Laughing over their escapades, Colin listened, eager to be included. Their antics made Colin smile and he said, "You lot could write a book, you've got more stories to tell than Catherine Cookson!"

Barbara, who lived close to the hospital, had been looking after Colin and the girls, bringing them sandwiches and drinks. "I'll bring you some colours back tonight if you like," she suggested.

Just as promised Barbara appeared with a plastic bag with all the tools they needed. A little manicure kit, including bright red polish.

Later that Thursday night, when the girls were sitting in their usual places at the top of MAC, Colin came down and said, "Isn't it time you girls were getting the show on the road?"

"Yes, if it's all right with you," they sang, eager to beautify Margaret.

In they went armed with laughter at the prospect of trying to make Margaret's nails glamorous. None of them had long nails, and they were novices at this sort of thing, but woe betide if they got the red polish on her fingers.

Kath removed the old stuff, Carole then massaged her hands with 'Angel', her favourite perfumed moisturiser, and then Christine began to paint. The giggles broke out, they talked to Margaret, asking her to keep her hands as still as possible for the task that they were undertaking. Margaret wasn't moving anyhow. Had she been conscious, Margaret would have languished in such pampering, as she'd always manicured her own hands.

One hand done, 'perfect' they thought, as they admired their handiwork.

Amidst the laughter, in came the sister, "Just checking on Margaret," she announced. But the girls thought differently. It must have been all the noise coming from the room that had caught her attention, and on entering they felt that they had to justify the strong smell of alcohol, from the nail varnish remover, so she wouldn't think that they had been drinking!

Colin was pleased and impressed with their work and the girls told him and Margaret that they would paint her toenails the following night.

Friday, was Mrs. Hand birthday, she did not want to acknowledge this whilst her daughter lay dying. She would rather take her place, she told Father Fraher on one of his visits.

The girls decided that they would attend Mass in the hospital chapel, which was just around the corner from MAC. The lovely Father Jennings told the small congregation that they would offer the Mass for Margaret, and for all the other people in the hospital.

At the end of the service, he gathered the three girls to him, and with arms across their shoulders he told the crowd that they had stayed with their friend since Tuesday. I call every morning to see how Margaret is doing and to say 'hello' to these great girls. "These girls are the **remnants of a youth club**. Their priest, Father Fraher opened a youth club for them and others over thirty-eight years ago, and they are all still good friends. Aren't they a credit to each other?"

Whilst they were driving to see Mrs. Hand to take her a gift for her birthday, Carole said, "Colin's right, you know, we should write a book."

"We could, couldn't we," remarked Kath.

Each of them was thinking the same, as Christine announced, "The title just has to be, *'Remnants of a Youth Club',* don't you think!"

They all agreed.

On their return to MAC, they sat with Margaret and Colin, reminiscing over past times once more. They were still laughing aloud, including Margaret in their conversation, when a young female doctor entered the room. They all felt embarrassed, to be giddy whilst Margaret rested quietly.

"Good, it is so nice to hear that you can manage to laugh at a time like this, it is the best medicine. Carry on. She will be able to hear you, I believe the hearing is the last of the senses to go," the doctor informed them.

She explained that she wanted to examine Margaret, and talk to Colin. And went on to say that because the weekend was upon them, they would need to make a decision regarding the best care for Margaret. MAC is a unit where the patients only stay either until a bed is available on a ward, or the patient improves and is discharged home. The plan was that later that day Margaret would be transferred to Ward 4, which is a medical ward.

The thought of this disturbed Colin, he felt any movement would upset her. He felt a little better when the staff informed him that she would be transferred on her bed.

Jean telephoned Mrs. Hand to wish her *'Happy Birthday'.* "I really don't know what to say, Mrs. Hand. I know it won't be a 'truly happy birthday' for you, but I have been thinking of you. We all have."

"I know love," said Mrs. Hand.

Jean continued the conversation by telling the elderly lady that Carole had telephoned most nights and that there'd been very little change.

"That's right love, she's been hanging on, she's only waiting for you, Jean."

At this Jean and Barrie made contingency plans. They would go to bed early and start their journey up North at 4:00 a.m. with hopes of arriving at Jean's sister Maureen's around nine o'clock.

Chapter Thirty-Seven

The upheaval of the disturbing bed shuffling rendered itself relevant and justified, as Margaret and her family were allocated a spacious room adjacent to the sister's office, which gave an instant feeling of security. This area was just before the entrance to the main ward giving privacy for relatives.

Kath and Carole accompanied Colin during the move to Ward 4 to give him some support. At this stage they felt Colin's needs were as important as Margaret's. The girls decided to go home and sleep that night, they did not know how long Margaret would continue to be with them, and tiredness was steadily descending upon them. But it was suggested by Kath and Carole that Christine should stay the night, if only to look after Colin.

She readily agreed, and appeared to have much more stamina than the other two. She was really a 'night owl', a nocturnal, not requiring much sleep.

The room was far less clinical than the one on MAC. The way it was decorated, and its position, gave it an appearance of being reserved for the terminally ill and the dying. Its soft peach lighting added a home from home cosy feel. There were important finishing touches too, pretty vases and pictures on the walls, not unlike that of an exclusive private hospital room.

Colin felt he'd been on a flitting, but the tranquillity brought him back to a calm relaxing level. Carole and Kath kissed Margaret, Colin and Christine goodnight, saying that they would return early in the morning. They hadn't yet managed to paint Margaret's toenails as promised, owing to the move, but there would be another day.

Ryan was last to leave, whispering to his mum that he would be back soon.

Colin's needs were met by the use of a deluxe Parker Knoll reclining chair, it being as comfy as any bed. The nurse brought blankets and a pillow in order for him to settle down for the night.

Christine left for the relative's room, just a few yards away. The room was grandly furnished with an inviting single bed, complete with duvet. It had a sofa, dining chairs and table and a kitchen area with tea and coffee facilities. She was grateful for this restful sanctuary. Being alone she missed her two buddies, but for the first time since Monday, she slept soundly.

It was only 5:45 a.m. when she sneaked into the room. Colin was still asleep, so she just held Margaret's hand and whispered sweet nothings to her, little things like that she was the best friend ever, and that she should come back to visit her when she got to heaven.

Alan called at seven o'clock on Saturday morning, after he had finished his night shift, to see if Christine wanted a lift home?

She declined his offer, saying that she would stay a while longer and get Peter to come for her. Carole came next on her way to start her shift, telling them that she would come back as soon as she was able.

Ryan arrived, kissing his mum and making idle chit-chat.

They were all talking, but Christine noticed that she did not hear Margaret breathe out after taking a long breath in.

She waved her hand at Colin and said in an unbelievably calm manner, "Colin come up to the bed, I think she's going."

Instantly, both Colin and Ryan were at opposite sides of Margaret, holding onto her, tears streaming down their faces.

"No, I can feel a pulse," Colin said sounding desperate.

Christine checked Margaret for a pulse. There was no sign of life; she told Colin it was his own pulse that he could feel, then she asked if they wanted her to leave?

"No, stay," Colin urged her gently.

So all three wept.

Christine went to inform the sister on the ward, whose face filled with tears, as she couldn't take it in. She had only just left Margaret herself, having just been in the room to check her medication; she felt so helpless. The nurse expressed genuine regard for this family, as she had a son Ryan's age and wouldn't like him to go through this dreadful experience. Colin left Margaret as the doctor and nurse came to certify her death. He made use of the time and telephone, informing everyone who needed to know.

Kath had just arrived alone, and Christine told her friend the news. Minutes later, Mick, Kath's husband arrived as he had heard the news from Colin and felt his wife would need him.

Jean and Barrie hit the road two hours before daybreak. Sleep had failed her, leaving her tired and full of apprehension. Her mind felt as though it had been hijacked, leaving her unable to think clearly. It was as though someone, or something alien had taken control of her world. Again and again she told herself, "This just isn't really happening," but of course it was! No matter how she tried to dismiss the thought, the death of her friend was imminent. It was so final that there was no turning back.

As the motorway network came to life and traffic passed at magnified speed, Jean's stomach felt like a brass band pumping and thumping. She felt physically sick. There were few words exchanged between the couple, and she wondered what sort of scene awaited them? From Carole's telephone calls she'd conjured up a picture, but dreaded the fate. She wondered whether any of the other motorists using this Northern route were on a similar mission as them – this mission of mercy.

Carole rang Maureen, Jean's sister, from her place of work at 8:15 a.m. to inform her that Margaret had been transferred to Ward 4 the previous night, and that she was peaceful, but otherwise there was no change.

"They're about an hour away," said Maureen. "I'll bring her up to the hospital though, don't worry."

"That's one less thing to think about," sighed Carole.

At nine o'clock, Carole was called from the ward and given the news. Tracey, one of the nurses on Deerplay

Ward kindly put her arms around Carole, took her into the office and told her she had taken a call from Christine to say that Margaret had died a few moments earlier. Her heart sank as Tracey expressed her sorrow and escorted her to Ward 4, so that she could pay her last respects and be with Colin, Ryan, Christine and Kath.

Carole cried silently as she walked aimlessly through the long hospital corridors. On the ward she met an outpouring of grief. The grief was both soundless and respectful. Yes, there were tears, but they were dignified, for Margaret wouldn't have had it any other way.

Carole shuddered at the thought of Jean being so close to Burnley. She rang Maureen who said that they had just arrived.

"I'll break the news," offered Maureen. "Can you ring me back in ten minutes?"

"Of course," said Carole in a quivering voice.

She rang later to say how sorry she was that they hadn't made it in time, and that this was what she had been afraid of all week. She spoke with weeping masking her voice.

"She must have known how I felt, I was dreading seeing her, I think she's spared me of everything," said Jean. "You girls have been so brave all week. I just couldn't have coped. I couldn't have faced it. I don't want to see her now. I just want to keep my last memories of her, of the time we shared when I was in Burnley last August. She looked brilliant then, like a million dollars."

"That's okay, Jean," Carole reassured her. "I just feel awful knowing that you were so near."

"No, no," said Jean. "Like I said, I think she knew how I felt."

Once back in the room Colin mentioned that the girls had not painted her toenails and Margaret would not like that. Willingly Christine offered to do this last thing for her friend. She went to ask the nurse for some tissues and when she got back in the room Colin had pulled the sheet up to reveal Margaret's unpainted toes. The feet were greyingly discoloured and cold to touch. Christine got to work, her hands shaking a little, but smiling incongruously she completed the pedicure to perfection.

Grateful for this task, Colin said that she could find a new trade here in this line of work, and laughingly suggested leaving a calling card. "You could be like Audrey Roberts out of Coronation Street, she works with the dead."

They both just smiled wanly. At this stage she left Colin alone with Margaret.

Before they all made their sad journeys home Colin had one last request from the girls on behalf of Margaret, and that was for one of them to be present when finally the news of her death was broken to her mother. Ryan quietly volunteered to go and tell his grandma, but Colin, being fully aware that Margaret's closest friends were considered Mrs. Hand's daughters, insisted that one of them go with him. It didn't need consultation, Kath and Mick offered immediately.

Mrs. Hand was up and dressed and sat in her high-backed chair by the window. On hearing car doors slam, she turned to see Ryan, Kath and Mick, walking with heads bowed up the path. As they stepped into the tiny living-room their mournful faces spoke volumes, not a word was necessary. The three of them crouched down to Mrs. Hand's level, weeping once more.

Through his tears Ryan whispered how peacefully his mum had died and how proud he was of her.

Mrs. Hand spoke out loud, "Eh lad it should have been me, what am I doing here at eighty-six?"

Later in the day at home, Peter directed Christine's gaze to a metal pail containing three beautiful bouquets of white roses, from Kathleen Lord for the three friends. It was her way of saying thank you for taking care of her friend, Margaret. Tears spilled and spilled.

Another caller came to the house, it was Elaine, Carole and Christine's younger sister, who had come to give her sisters her support. She handed Christine two sympathy cards, one for her and one for Carole. She then brought two half bottles from her bag, whisky for Christine and Bacardi for Carole, hoping that perhaps the contents might bring them both a little comfort and some much needed rest. She hadn't known what else to do!

Knowing just how little spare money Elaine actually had, the cards and bottles were such a wonderful gesture. Hugging Elaine closely, and thanking her sincerely, Christine went to bed and cried herself to sleep.

Peter played the messenger delivering the other two bouquets to Kath and to his sister-in-law, Carole. He also left the Bacardi from Elaine with Carole. Her sister's generosity and thoughtfulness also hit Carole hard, and tears spilled down once more.

Arrangements had been made to meet Jean later that evening, she too was going to bed to rest for the afternoon after her seamless drive up North.

They just had to be together, the girls. Oh husbands offered comfort and support, but it was different for them. It was as if they needed to cling onto each other, knowing that they all felt the same pain, that they all shared the same grief. The grief that had been secretly sealed over in recent months and needed to be unlocked and allowed to overspill. Margaret had meant so much to all of them in individual ways, that they feared being without her.

They needed a change of scenery, somewhere refreshing, where they were anonymous, and a place that felt different to them, not holding any previous memories of earlier visits with Margaret.

The place they chose was a bistro in the town of Clitheroe, which is tucked under the shadow of Pendle Hill. Yet again, it was Carole who was the driver, not wanting to have much to drink, just a glass of wine.

Seated around a small table, four middle-aged women, surrounded by throngs of youngsters enjoying the atmospheric mood of the busy bar, relived the week in which they had watched their friend pass away. Memories not too difficult to talk about, were the focus of the night. Making plans to keep close contact with Jean who had to make the return journey South the following morning, only too aware of the funeral which loomed in the week ahead.

"I have to be back for work on Monday, and then drive back up on Wednesday. Well not me literally but Barrie, he's ever so good," said Jean, gratefully.

The other three had each other to use as a crutch, but Jean was too far away for hugs. Promises of more telephone calls were made, and a decision had been reached to go to Stratford as planned; it would have been what Margaret wanted. A date was made for early March.

Wine had been used to try and douse the weeping, but all it had done was to ignite despairing feelings. Kath was emotionally wrecked. The tears fell, releasing the exclamation of sorrow which had been suppressed throughout the week. Jean had already been taken to Maureen's, but the sisters knew better than to take Kath home to Mick in this wretched state, so coffee and a listening ear were on the menu. Once she was calm and collected, Carole drove her home to an anxiously waiting husband.

Chapter Thirty-Eight

Colin had honourably arranged a funeral car for the girls and their husbands. So it was outside number 1, Richmond Street, on Friday morning that they met with Colin, a man whose heart had been broken, though today he would be strong and proud for everyone's sake.

The autumnal rising mist and clear blue sky gave a deceitful illusion of springtime. It wasn't cold, damp or wet. There was no howling wind or biting frost, or was there? Only the mourners could not feel it, because of the pain which engulfed them. The girls had made a pact, they would each wear some fake leopard-skin which Margaret had had a fancy for.

The black velvet hat which Christine wore was trimmed with leopard-skin. Margaret had given this to her the previous winter saying she was a hat person, so she'd suit it, and Christine regarded this as special. Kath indulged in the leopard-skin collar, over her ankle-length winter coat; again it had been a gift from Margaret on their return from Oxford, a gift that she held dear to her heart. A flimsy voile leopard print scarf was wound around Carole's neck, adding glamour to her new, black, Danimac raincoat. Jean's leopard-skin wool gloves kept the cold out for her. Each felt they wore the fakery emblem out of symbolic respect for a very courageous lady.

Margaret would have been proud of her men in dark suits and ties. It seemed somewhat strange at her house, people were buzzing in and out of the opened front door. Faded conversations were taking place, just out of politeness, as a necessity, to pass the time. People, friends and neighbours had begun to line Richmond Street, marking respect, and ready to say their goodbyes to this wonderful person. It was whilst waiting for the cortège, that the four friends revisited memory lane. Each of them delving into Pandora's Box, releasing precious memories of different times.

Margaret received a funeral fit for a princess. White lilies laid with greenery, spread the length and width of her coffin which stood proudly at the front of St. Teresa's Roman Catholic Church. The church was filled to capacity emulating her life here on earth. Of course, she wasn't a saint by any means, but a loveable person with her feet planted firmly on the ground, with no 'hairy-fairy pie in the sky' rubbish, but enough collective qualities to build a reputation for friendship.

Each mourner attending the Requiem Mass was moved by different parts of it, whilst singing to the old-fashioned hymns which Mrs. Hand, who was unable to attend, had chosen for her daughter. These hymns took the girls back to the old primary school-days of St. Mary Magdalene's and their senior school days at St. Hilda's.

Father Fraher extended his sympathy to her family and friends, offering consolation as he paid his own sincere tributes to Margaret.

Brenda, Mrs. Hand's friend and cleaner stayed with her from morning till night, so that she wasn't alone, during this black day.

The most poignant action one will always remember was like something transfixed, as the cortège slowly passed by the shops and businesses on Coal Clough Lane, where Margaret was loved and remembered by the proprietors and customers alike. As a mark of respect, doors were closed and crowds lined the lane, with gentlemen holding their caps across their breasts, heads bowed like in bygone days. They stood straight and silent, and as tall as trees, while the cars slowly made their way towards Burnley cemetery, where Margaret would be laid to rest with Leonard, her father.

A lengthy row of cars formed a slow procession stretching into the depths of Burnley Cemetery, escorted by many mourners on foot. Poignant memories flashed through minds as they passed marked gravestones of deceased family and friends' graves which had been tended with loving care. Some had been there for three decades and more.

The burial site was favourably chosen twenty-years previously by Margaret and her mum when they had laid Mr. Hand to rest. The persuasion being the graceful drooping branches of a particular tree, sometimes known as the weeping lady of the woods. A crowd stood shivering in the grounds for the sun was receding now; it was no longer bright and warm, but dull and old like an old man's medal, in need of a polish.

Janine, the Trickett girls' youngest sister, along with Elaine, were amongst them. Standing with her one-year old daughter's pushchair, and being only six weeks away from her confinement date with her third child, Janine looked pale, tired, cold and sad. She'd walked the two miles from her home in Padiham to pay her last respects.

A mixture of life-long influences spread around the graveside where faces portrayed a vision of empathy for the chief mourners. Anne, Kristine and Veronica stood arms linked, shoulders haunched and collars up, braving the elements which were now foreboding with whisking winds. These girls were not only friends from the youth club but belonged to Mrs. Peel's army of long ago. On the tarmac path huddled together were Christine and Barbara from the Mecca days.

Kath spotted Sheila, the babysitter at whose venue the teenage parties had been hosted. She lifted her hand in acknowledgement, her thoughts wondering where on earth time had gone, as though cataloguing the years. Yet just now her memory felt like a vacuum devoid of all existence. Joan her sister, who had supported them throughout the week prior to Margaret's death had made her way to the place so close to Little Cornwall, the area where she was raised.

All felt honoured for having been part of Margaret's life, but the highest honour and privilege was bestowed upon her family. Her mum, husband and her children. Jean, Kath, Christine and Carole were proud to be members of that extended family. Everyone gathered there reflected as Father Fraher, the family priest and friend, recited the last lament, all sharing the same realisation that love lasts forever and as the great balladeer sings, *'Love, love changes everything, how we live and how we die!'*

We personally know this to be true, for the four of us so loved Margaret, just as she loved each of us. For us, all the sweet memories are blessings that will remain with each one of us forever.

Throughout our lives, we will each ensure that there will always be a surviving trace of Margaret, for it is love and friendship that link together the *remnants of a youth club.*

THE AUTHORS